# THE OCEAN RIVER

# THE SUN,
# THE SEA,

---

# AND TOMORROW

F. G. WALTON SMITH

AND HENRY CHAPIN

# The Sun,
# the Sea,
# and Tomorrow

POTENTIAL SOURCES OF

FOOD, ENERGY AND MINERALS

FROM THE SEA

CHARLES SCRIBNER'S SONS  NEW YORK  1954

# CONTENTS

# ILLUSTRATIONS

# Foreword

## BY CHARLES F. KETTERING

OF RECENT YEARS MANY BOOKS HAVE
been written on the growth of human population and on the
limitations of the land to cope with it in terms of food, fuel
and minerals. In many of these books it has been stated that
there are limitless reserves of food and minerals in the sea,
but beyond vague generalizations the actual part to be
played by the sea has not been discussed. It is timely therefore that the role of the sea as a provider of mineral and
food wealth should at last be given book-length treatment.

To a practical scientist and engineer it is refreshing to see
that food and fuel are here regarded as they should be—as
two different aspects of the same thing, for they are both
sources of energy. The overall picture of our energy use,
abuse and future needs is here brought into focus as a
background for the examination of the ocean as a new
frontier of supply.

The sun is our only permanent energy source, and much
loose thinking has grown up because of failure to realize
this. The relation of food and fuel to the sun is clearly
brought out in this book.

The ocean as a vast pastureland and a limitless reservoir of minerals is not to be tamed immediately. The authors caution against any belief that wealth is there for the taking. On the other hand they realize that new and unexpected ways of doing things are the products of sustained research, and that research itself must not be restrained by the belief that "it cannot be done."

We cannot see at present how we are going to use the thinly scattered resources of the sea. But this itself is a challenge to man's "know how." The obvious pressure of world wide population growth, already moving at explosive pace, forbids us to shelve this challenge as anything except immediate and urgent.

# THE SUN,
# THE SEA,

---

# AND TOMORROW

# CHAPTER 1

# The Loaves
# and the Fishes

FROM THE EARLIEST TIMES MAN HAS
called the earth Mother and like an infant has taken for
granted that the earth would nourish and sustain him, come
what may. He has been avid to discover and quick to squan-
der the seemingly inexhaustible riches of the earth and has
then cried out in alarm as fresh waves of population consumed the wealth he had considered inexhaustible. Henry
Adams put this neatly in saying: "History shows man as al-
ternately insane with his pride of intellect, and shuddering
with horror at its bloody consequences."

In recent years the human race has been going through
a phase of tremendous growth in numbers with an expansion
of more than half again since the first of the present century. This raid on the world's larder has begun to tell. The
problem of how to find more food, more minerals and more
power to satisfy mounting demands has recently been
handled in several thoughtful and a few hysterical books.
Some of these authors have, more or less in passing, hopefully pointed to the ocean as the last relatively unexploited

area of the globe which might meet the urgent demands of the human rabbit warren. What are the facts and what is the truth concerning the fertility of the vast expanse of oceans and its suspended mineral wealth? Can we expect the sea to pick up the dinner check for the hungry world when our farms and chemical food factories and our mines can no longer do so? We must find out.

We intend to examine with a critical eye the potentialities of the sea, the extent of its natural wealth and its availability, as a last frontier, of relatively unexploited resource. But before we do this we must take a brief look at the situation we now face in regard to crops and minerals and sources of energy as affected by the pressure of modern populations. John Boyd Orr, former chief of the Food and Agricultural Organization of the United Nations, puts the problem quite simply: "The rising tide of population and the falling reservoir of food resources constitute . . . the greatest issue facing mankind today. There will be no peace in the world as long as half of its people suffer from hunger and poverty, knowing that food in abundance is entirely possible."

There is no argument here. But there are many arguments as to how we can go about solving the increasing imbalance between supply and demand; whether by greater and swifter exploitation of the world's resources or by some miraculous devices of chemistry in a brave new world of the future or by a present disciplined control of the run-away fertility of the human race. Intriguing arguments can be brought up to support all of these solutions but none, we think, that alone will fully answer the problem of present want and future starvation. We think man at least should know what to expect if he turns to the sea with all his technological and scientific skills in an attempt to replenish his larder and to find renewable sources of minerals and energy. It is true that we have in the sea the vast fertility of its invisible pastures and the billions of tons of mineral wealth in solution. But it is not an easy frontier, no bonanza such as the Western Hemisphere presented to the desperate needs of the fifteenth century. Yet we may be obliged to turn to it as our land resources shrink.

For about three hundred years in the New World the surplus European populations, moving into the vacuum of a vast and virgin frontier of new land, have been able to hack and hew and hunt and plant and dig and use up everything they had a mind to lay their hands on. The peoples of Europe, with a great new world ahead of them, set out to conquer nature and the western wilderness. According to their own definitions they have. But nature as a living force pushed into a corner becomes highly explosive. As we now rest our aching backs, admire our machines and survey our conquered domain we discover that we have wasted, consumed or wantonly destroyed a goodly portion of our inheritance. The western frontier of free land and windfall wealth is closed. The land is fenced, the wealth is carefully incorporated. So, from being exploiters of seemingly limitless natural resources on land we have become stewards of a limited domain.

Before Columbus, the population of Europe had been fairly stationary for centuries. With a fixed area of land for growing food and fuel, the forces of human reproduction pressed hard on the heels of what was not much more than bare subsistence, judged by our own present standards of living. The daily birth rate, the inexorable flood of too many

*Figure 1.* Natural Fertility of the World. Only a few areas have a natural high fertility, and many areas are almost worthless.

new arrivals was evenly balanced by death from famine, plague and pestilence. But with Columbus, there came new lands and natural resources to create new energies and to remove these checks and barriers. This was only the beginning. With Africa and Australia added to the New World, a great new land frontier was opened up with food

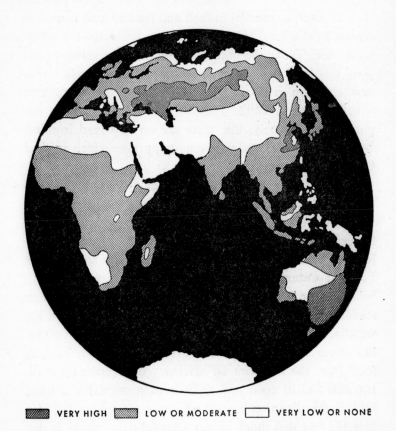

VERY HIGH    LOW OR MODERATE    VERY LOW OR NONE

and mineral wealth for those who were willing to work for it.

European humanity, no longer checked by the famine and pestilence and war engendered by land poverty and crowded conditions, slowly began the great expansion which is at its peak today. By the early part of the twentieth century the ratio of mouths to feed and land to feed them had returned to the level of Columbus's day. We were back where we started. Today the population increase has gone far beyond this level of balance between land and people and a new situation is arising in many ways parallel to that which existed in 1492. There is a difference, a most important one, namely, that there are no new land frontiers comparable in size and productivity to those which awaited Columbus.

It is easy to be lulled into an attitude of mind which rejects the situation as unreal or exaggerated. We see around us, in the Western world, no great shortage of food or manufactured goods, except during the stress of war, and we listen with too little conviction to the voices of such men as Fairfield Osborn, William Vogt and others who seek to bring the problem into public focus. We do have a high standard of living, better in purely material ways than the wealthiest could command in Columbus's time. Much of this has come from agricultural development which extracts food from the soil with an efficiency once undreamed of. But this has its costs and there is unquestionably a finite limit in this direction beyond which we cannot go. We also face the fact that much of our vaunted daily plenty is due to a vastly improved technical ability to mine and manufacture and use up the nonrenewable, fast dwindling resources of the mine. The end to this approaches. And outside of our own strip of earth, peoples of other countries are dying daily of starvation and malnutrition.

We do not deny the possibilities exist, on land alone, for entirely new solutions to this problem—when man gets around to them. But, except for a brief review of our present world-wide position and the possible future of the land, our purpose here is to chart the potentials of the ocean and to see what we may realistically expect it to yield in our search for a new world frontier. It is here that some profess to see an almost unlimited source of mineral and vegetable resources which only awaits our skill to free them for a hungry world. It is a job quite as tough and equally as urgent as the taming of any previous wilderness.

Man is the recipient of various bounties stemming from the source of all life, the radiant energy of the sun. Its eternal radiation is translated to our use as food, for instance, by the green magic of photosynthesis. This flow of energy is perpetual but its limitations for mankind are fixed by the boundaries of our land and its fertile acres. Our land can feed us only in proportion to the demands we make upon it, but there is an upper limit to what it can yield. In spite of modern science and a well-fed America, we are as haunted by the presence of starvation today as we were some hundreds of years ago in the closed frontiers of a European world. The uncontrolled fertility of man opposes the limited fertility of the earth he treads. Perhaps, as some think, the way out is to turn to the sea and to change this from its present hunter's realm to a salt area of cultivation and harvest which can stay the world's need.

Our mineral wealth, as well as our food supply, is on the wane. But what is even more serious, it is nonrenewable. Minerals are concentrated in rich but circumscribed pockets and they do not renew themselves each year with the sun and the spring, in the way our crops do. Much of them have already disappeared for ever. Where have they gone? For the most part they are reduced to perishable construction

NORTHERN HEMISPHERE

*Figure 2.* (Coker, Pg. 65) To show distribution of land and water in the Northern and Southern hemispheres.

---

or unworkable rubbish which by natural courses will drain into the sea. There it remains as an immense reservoir of dilute mineral wealth. So, with increasing frequency the question is asked: how can we mine the ocean reservoir?

We live by grace of one other natural bounty. Besides our

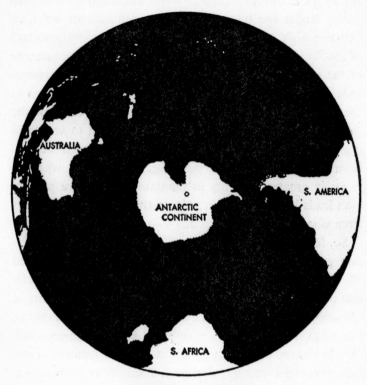

SOUTHERN HEMISPHERE

minerals and the food energy of our crops and herds, we rely upon power for the energy to heat our houses, to drive our machines and to speed us on our way across and above the land and sea. What of our coal and oil and natural gas? These are the fossil fuels, formed by the fixed energy of the sun stored in our mines and oil wells. These too are fast dissipating under the booming prodigal demands of what we call our high standard of living. This increasing standard of available wealth per person today is too often the measure of the rapid consumption of a fixed resource, of nonrenewable capital. When mineral fuels are gone we must turn to the atomic nucleus and to some unexploited form of the sun's energy to live and this leads back again to vegetable photosynthesis, which has its limits on land but has scarcely been touched in the vast pasturage of the seas, where it exists in greatest quantity as plankton. The future path of man leads back, at least in part, to the shores of the waters from whence he first emerged.

So, for the equation of hunger, we know it will not maintain even its present precarious level without disciplined effort by individual nations and, beyond that, commercial and political cooperation within the United Nations. Part of this cooperation should include a more thorough exploration of availiable energies within and beneath the seas that have been used commonly by international agreement of one kind or another for many ages past. Scientists and economists are correct in pointing out that there is no sudden panacea or any such windfall of riches awaiting oceanic development comparable to the development of the New World during the past two centuries. But there is enough to make a valuable difference and perhaps offer a final solution.

We see an end to the nonrenewable fuels, the energy sources derived from the mine. Just when the end will come we do not know, but the limit is a finite one, probably within a few generations, depending on the increasing rate at which we use them and the success of exploration for the remaining stocks of this capital wealth. The faster we find this capital, unfortunately, the sooner we shall spend it, for this is the profligate way of human beings. We see, too, an upper limit or ceiling to the rate at which we can produce our renewable resources, principally of course, our food. It is also obvious that in spite of optimistic faith in the possibility of future accomplishments in agricultural chemistry and biology technology, the grim fact remains that we have not been able to increase the production of food sufficiently to supply even the present world population adequately. And we must remember that every day 70,000 extra mouths are joining us for dinner.

Today our food and our energy come mainly from the land, and the land covers less than two-fifths of the earth's surface. So let us look to the sea, the shallow shores and the great oceans, averaging two miles in depth. It is perfectly true that there are great sources of food and minerals in the seas, and even of energy if we can find out how to use them. What are the chances that this can be done? And how will this affect us? Will it merely put off the evil day when we shall discover that all nonrenewable resources are used up, or will we find a practical renewable source of minerals and energy as well as food?

The development of new frontiers of scientific investigation in the watery three-fifths of the globe's surface is an exciting prospect facing modern man. The great problem for man in oceanic food production is not so much a matter of discovery as of devising scientific and mechanical means for harvesting a crop that is vast, dilute and scattered but present in difficult abundance.

We know that minerals abound in the waters of the ocean.

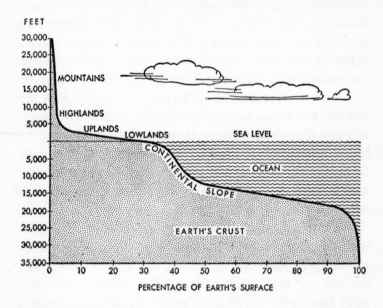

*Figure 3*. The percentage shown at any point is the amount of the earth's surface which is higher in altitude than that point. Thus only about 30 per cent of the earth is higher than sea level, and only 50 per cent is above a depth of 10,000 feet below sea level.

---

We know that there are floating pastures of minute vegetation of high food value. We know that it is possible in tidal areas to harness the very energy of the rise and fall of the sea and even use the temperature differences between surface and very deep water to provide energy for mankind. We are also on the verge of being able to transform useful quantities of salt water into fresh water along arid coastal areas of the earth. All these interesting possiblities lie at our door today. But—and this is our problem—the availability and production of new sources of energy, which in themselves are great, bring no solution to the fate of mankind unless the equation between new mouths and new provender is kept in control. The simple scientific inventory of the problem immediately calls forth parallel advances in social, political and even theological thinking. In the following chapters our task will be to make as unprejudiced an inventory as possible of present and future resources available under the seas and to take stock of this new frontier of scientific development. In doing this we must perforce consider the possibilities of new energy, food and mineral sources from the land, but they will take second place to our prime purpose, the survey of the possibilities of the new sea frontier of science and industry.

# CHAPTER 2

# The Salt Wheel of Life

WHEN MAN WAS A HUNTER AND HAD to search and forage, stalk and waylay his next meal, never sure in the wilderness of land and sea where his daily bread or blood would be found, we call him primitive. Hunger was his companion and chance his hope. He lived in apprehension of different hazards from those that beset civilized man. He was not concerned with problems of yield per acre, soil erosion, fertilizers, crop rotation or soil chemistry. He lived by the testimony of his senses without production statistics, accepting what we call the natural rhythm of life. He had to. But civilization has marched on. We, as land animals, have come at length to what we call the conquest of nature. With increasing numbers to nourish and with the concentration of human beings into tribal communities, the scattered booty of nature began to be insufficient.

So, in our progress from primitive life to industrial civilization we have become first, farmers and then chemists and engineers. We fence in, cultivate, hew down, fertilize and artificially—that is, with agricultural art—control or steer nature into greater benefits to man. Science has done away with the hunter on land. We pulverize the very rocks and scrape the dung from under the birds of the sea to intensify the yield of our cultivated acres.

In many ways the cycles of life, of land, and sea, run closely parallel. The oceans, just as the lands, have their pastures with a constantly fluctuating vegetable life which sustains, from invisible life to the largest whale, a myriad animal horde which grazes and shears through the living waters. The same chemistry of fertilizers is necessary to support this life both on land and in the sea. But, in our attempts to assess the value of the ocean to mankind as a scientific frontier for the development of more food, the analogy is not always obvious. As land creatures we would scarcely be able to recognize most of the sea plants as vegetation at all while, paradoxically, some of the sea animals have themselves every appearance of being plants. Most of the plants are not even visible to the naked eye. Man, as yet, is a stranger to many of the teeming forms of life hidden in the welter of the seas.

These differences have retarded man from the conquest of the vast regions of the under-sea. So far, he has done little to cultivate this storehouse, and his civilization and mechanical arts have paused at the shore or upon the surface of the shallower seas. There are, of course, some small exceptions to this but these are a mere beginning. In various parts of the world he has learned to cultivate oysters and sponges. Even fishes are being raised in captivity. But these are a small fraction only of the full harvest of the sea. Our entire crop of sea food today is a mere fraction of 1 per cent of the full measure of growth in the sea. We reap without sowing. We are still merely the hunters of a wilderness under the waters. Here we have done little to extend man's conquest of nature in contrast to the visible achievements on land where so much has been done both to answer old wants and to create new horizons of existence. We can still be defined as primitive huntsmen when it comes to the ocean for its vast dilute stores of wealth have largely escaped our grasp.

The very extent of the sea and the diffuse plenty of life within it present a frontier for man's ingenuity quite different from the land frontiers we have so thoroughly explored. The full extent of the world's oceans is half again as great as the land areas of the world. But size alone does not account for all the difference, although the depths of the marine biosphere, or habitable area for life, supply 300 times the living room offered by land and fresh-water areas together. Ocean plant life can survive as deep as the rays of the sun are able to penetrate, in contrast to the few inches of soil area which constitute the useful depth of land. In addition to this, much of the land areas consist of barren deserts or great polar ice caps. Life in the ocean reproduces itself wherever the sun reaches and penetrates. It is not surprising, therefore, that biological oceanographers have calculated that nearly 90 per cent of the world's total vegetation is produced, largely unseen by man, beneath the salt surface of the seas. But when we add together the total of his catch, we see that man has made available to himself only a small part of the provision of the sea which might be his were he able to harvest and exploit its riches with the efficiency of his production on land. So here we have truly an unexploited, resistant frontier challenging the mechanical and scientific skills of the future.

What are the chances of breaking through this hunter's rhythm and governing for man's use the scattered and dilute bounty of salt water? The science of oceanography, combining as it must the fruits of geological, chemical, biological and even meteorological research, has in the past fifty years clearly defined the problem. It is truly only a beginning, a frontier, but one of rich possibilities beyond our present ability to apply present knowledge to practical ends. The science of sea life must be pushed and developed to the extent that we have already developed the parallel sciences of agriculture, agronomics and animal husbandry. And first of all, we must begin this inventory of food potential from the sea by considering the web of life in the oceans, the chemical and biological facts of what we might call ocean agriculture. This should show both the exciting possibilities, as well as the present difficulties and practical limitations, which accompany the full exploitation of the pastures and prairies of the salt world hidden beneath the waves.

The basic principles, as always, may be stated rather simply. The details of applying these principles to specific cases are more complex. We start with the sun, our prime source of energy, and we end with the burning and consumption of food-fuels within our own bodies, a process which provides the energy necessary for muscular movement, for our nervous activity and for the continuance of life itself. Most of our food is used for this. Somewhere about one-tenth of it goes for growth. Without this energy from the sun, subtly transformed in various ways to our uses, life would cease.

Whatever its outward form, whether on land or sea, from a chemical standpoint food as human fuel is basically the same. It consists of complicated forms of carbon compounded with other elements. Our bodies are delicate machines for breaking down those compounds of elements which are necessary for our growth. Fish, fowl, meat and vegetation are all grist to the mill or, better, fuel for the furnace of our body cells which take in and transform this energy. This down-grading from a higher to a lower potential of energy takes place just as wood, full of the stored energy of the sun transformed originally by photosynthesis, when burned releases heat and in so doing is changed to such products of combustion as carbon dioxide and water. These end-products have no energy left immediately useful to man. They go back into the great reservoir of the air. Here they are again available in the cycle for change into living trees, but only after an addition of new energy from the sun by the, as yet, unsolved processes of photosynthesis. In the same way we depend on the ability of other plants as chemical laboratories to transform the living rays of light and the inert elements of earth and air into vital food for man and beast. And this, in turn, releases living energy as it is broken up by our bodies to carbon dioxide and water. The sun is thus perpetually recharging the battery of energy that sustains mankind.

This cycle differs little on land or under the sea so that we can talk of it for the moment as a single universal process. Plant life in the sea as well as in the air has its leaf-factories for the operation wherein chlorophyll absorbs sunlight and converts simple substances into essential chemical energy.

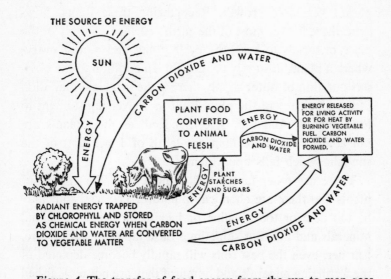

*Figure 4.* The transfer of food energy from the sun to man goes through a cycle in which carbon dioxide of the air is changed to plant fuel or food and then to animal food. By burning or by life processes the carbon dioxide is again released. It can then enter the cycle again when green plants absorb more solar energy.

This completes a never-ending cycle when the food it builds up is consumed and dissipated into waste products.

Carbon dioxide, of course, is present in the sea just as in the air in sufficient quantities for plants to grow. In fact, sea water holds 100 times more carbon dioxide than an equal volume of air. On the land there is the further determining factor of the presence or absence of water in the soil in sufficient quantity to support growth. There are large parts of the earth where lack of rainfall or permanent ice-caps do not permit vegetable growth. Recognizing these limits, however, there is over most of the earth's surface a supply of the basic materials to keep the cycle going and almost everywhere a plentiful supply of sunlight. In addition to the obvious question of water supply there is the principal limitation of the efficiency of the plant itself in converting sunlight to food energy. And this is low, indeed, as most plants are not able to use more than one-tenth of 1 per cent of the sunlight which falls upon them.

There are other factors which hold back the growth of plants and these are chemical in nature. The land soils may be too acid or too alkaline or lacking in certain essential minerals and are thus sometimes unsuitable for agriculture. Further, even the best soils will rapidly become depleted of the fertilizing minerals and humus if they are not replenished one way or another. Phosphorus and nitrogen compounds principally, and also a number of substances or trace elements needed in lesser quantities, are vital to life and growth although they are not the prime carriers of energy. Most of these are constantly leaching away and being carried by stream and river to the remote reservoir of the oceans.

When we talk about the relationship of minerals and fertilizers to plant life on land, we are talking largely in terms of man made conditions where the science and mechanics of agriculture have altered and controlled the natural rhythm of life to enhance the immediately useful output of food, fuel or fibers. Herein the problem differs from our exploitation of the seas which, we have pointed out, is still largely in the hunting stage beyond the artificial controls of man. On undeveloped land, it is true, there is a normal or virgin balance between the soil and the fertilizing minerals which are absorbed by plants and again returned to the soil in an uninterrupted cycle when the unharvested dead vegetable matter or humus is rotted and reabsorbed into the seedbeds. But when man breaks into this cycle and captures, through cultivated crops, the minerals and other compounds, they do not again, except as animal manure, return to the soil but are flushed down our sewage systems. Even more of the artificial fertilizer added by man is washed away by rain, and in brooks and streams and rivers it makes the long journey to the sea. This must be replaced from other mineral sources which, as we know, are large but not inexhaustible. The rhythm has been broken. We have not yet learned the answer of how to reverse this one-way hourglass of waste, and time is running out in relation to man's uncontrolled production of hungry human mouths. We have been fortunate to discover rich deposits of mineral fertilizers, phosphates and nitrates, laid down in the dim geological past as sediments of ancient ocean floors. But this is capital and, once consumed, returns to the ocean world where it remains for the most part unavailable to man. Our race may not be here to benefit by current deposits in this oceanic bank at present locked against us by the depth of the seas.

To sum it up, there is a food cycle on land in which carbon dioxide and water, together with the essential elements such as phosphorus, are converted by the energy of the sun's rays into vegetable crops. These form our meadows, pasture land and the fields of our farms. Crops in turn support animal herds which are consumed by man. Whether used as food or fuel for heating, the constituent elements are not lost but are returned as gas, water or ash to the reservoir of the atmosphere, or, as in the case of phosphorus and other elements, make a one-way trip to that other great reservoir, the sea.

The cycle of life from a chemical standpoint is basically the same in what we can call the aquasphere of the oceans as in the soil. The chemical, physical and biological processes which sustain life in such very different environments, however, present separate problems. We find the ocean has its own kinds of meadows and fertile plains of rich vegetation where the animal herbivores of the sea graze and forage. There is, also, beneath the waters a fiercely competitive battle where carnivores hunt and consume the grazing animals and each other. No one can long doubt this who has watched great schools of mullet leap in panic from their native element for a second of safety in the sun when harassed by shark or barracuda, or schools of giant tuna in the Pacific shoot up out of the sea before the attack of killer whales. The same plant chemistry that traps the sunlight on land also sustains this wild sea-life but not in any form the average farmer or landsman would recognize. Few men other than marine biologists have seen at firsthand the minute grazing cattle of the ocean pastures.

What sort of browse and vegetation are the meadows and prairies of the ocean, that are so much greater in extent than any we know on land? The most obvious ones we see at the edges of the watery world are the seaweeds. Just below the tidemarks we can see the dark fronds and arms of the wrack and the kelp, swaying beyond the surf anchored to the rocks and buoyed up toward the sunlight by their bladders of air. Some of the greater kelps offshore stream their leaves a hundred feet or more as they reach towards the surface.

These all have been harvested, for food or fertilizer or for the agar-agar and the iodine which they contain. In the Orkneys there is even a small breed of sheep that eats this ocean vegetation. Seaweeds are fed to cattle in Japan where the people likewise make gelatinous dishes from the smaller shore varieties. But this is a very small part indeed of the available food from the sea, for the shore weeds amount to far less than 1 per cent of the total vegetable growth of the oceans and can never have any great significance as an adequate source of food for man. This is bad luck because, of all sea vegetation, the seaweeds are the easiest to reap, as we shall later describe.

The true frontiers of marine agriculture have only been revealed to man within the past seventy-five years. Until modern times the sea has remained in history and literature a great immutable mystery beyond man's comprehension. Today the combined sciences of oceanography, starting with the famous voyage of the H.M.S. Challenger in 1872–6, have revealed the depth, the fertility and the kinds of life that teem beneath the surface of the sea. The real vegetable producers of the ocean are so small that for the most part they are individually invisible and only to be seen by man when sifted from the water through a fine silken net to be viewed under a microscope. Yet they thrive and spread from the Arctic to the Equator all over the seas. It is an odd truth that the giant algal plants, the accessible seaweeds close to shore are of small importance as a food source compared to the invisible microscopic plants of the open seas. The answer lies in the dependence of plants upon light.

The contrast of environment between land and sea has much to do with this. On land, for instance, the activity of plants is confined to a thin atmospheric layer bounded below by the earth and above by a height of the vegetable growth that might average twenty-five feet. At sea the layer of possible growth is deeper, extending from the surface of the water as far below as the light will penetrate. This depth under good conditions may be several hundred feet, although the most efficient depths are less than two hundred. The seaweeds, as we have shown, can only inhabit the shallow coastal waters because they are anchored, much as land plants and so are limited in mobility. Were they anchored to deeper bottoms they would be out of range of the sun. But the vast pastures of the open sea are not so limited by ties to the shore for they drift buoyantly in the sunlit layers of water over the entire ocean, independent of a sea floor for anchorage. Nor are they encumbered with heavy skeletons subject to the pull of gravity, for they lie suspended in an equable climate, one might say almost a salt womb of nourishment, so alike are their vital juices to the salt water which supports and surrounds them.

This we shall describe in greater detail when we take up the plants which compose this drifting pasturage. For the moment we look at the most obvious characteristics of vegetable plankton. Plankton, by the way, is a word derived from the Greek denoting the fact that these are drifting life. Vegetables in the plankton are minute single-celled plants invisible to the naked eye. This, of course, accounts for the great difficulty of harvesting such a crop, however abundant, unless the special instrument for their capture is furnished by nature. This does occur in the guise of the plankton herbivores, the grazing animal plankton, and herein lies one of the notable differences between the grazing populations on land and in the sea, for the seagoing herbivores, counterparts of cows and horses, elephants and deer, are not easily seen with the naked eye. Under the microscope one of the strangest sights on earth is to see the weird and extraordinarily diverse forms nature has taken in forming the plankton, particularly the zooplankton, the small animals which consume the vegetable plankton.

One would think that creation was in a singularly active experimental stage to look at the zooplankton hauled up in a net. Here we see prototypes of every strange figment of man's imagination, equipped with a great variety of mechanisms for floating in different densities of water and with a hundred types of minute sieves and devices for trapping and digesting the vegetation they consume in such quantity. The largest of these are sometimes almost an inch in length but for the most part escape the eye of an observer. In their nightmare miniature world they look like arrows, balloons, tiny shrimps and animals which a painter like Heronimus Bosch might have conceived, with their many legs, hairy spines, delta-shaped wings or lace umbrellas. For the most part the animal plankton consists of many-legged, spiny shrimplike creatures, the smaller ones known as copepods, and the larger kind, growing to the size of about an inch, as euphausids. These, unlike the floating plants, have a limited power of movement through the water.

The animal plankton in turn is hunted by a few of the fishes such as herring and menhaden and by the young of many others which have developed special equipment for such minute provender. The huge whales live almost entirely on this kind of prey, sifting through the whalebone fringes and curtains of their great mouths a flood of water con-

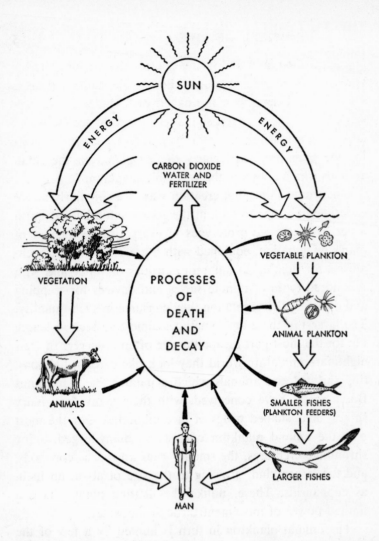

*Figure 5*. The chain of fertility in the sea is longer and more complex than on the land. For purposes of simplification this diagram omits the part played by bottom animals, crabs, oysters and the like.

taining the swarms of tiny food creatures. But, on the whole, most adult fish have no such mechanism for straining the sea water so that they in turn are obliged to feed upon the plankton-feeders, thus establishing a pyramid of life and energy starting with the vegetable plankton, then the small animal plankton, then the fishes that consume them and finally by one or more stages to the big fishes that eat the little fishes.

One of the obvious facts that strikes us in viewing this lengthy chain of food production in the sea is that the end-product is dependent on a succession of circumstances that anywhere may be affected or interrupted to make a poor crop at the end of the chain, in the realm of the larger fishes where man finds seafood most available.

The problem of accurately estimating the food potential of the oceans is not merely limited to a study of the natural plankton population but must also take into account a temporary or guest population of larvae, eggs and small-fry of the larger fishes which for a while assume a planktonic existence. They drift sustained by the ocean currents but helpless and available as food for zooplankton and their own adult kind. Most fishes release their eggs directly into the water, small and unprotected. The great bluefin tuna, which attains a weight of five hundred to a thousand pounds, has offspring no longer than one-quarter of an inch in length. So, added to other forms of plankton are vast shoals of baby fishes which are just as much a part of the ocean's floating population, until they begin to grow and prey upon their infant associates, as are the shrimplike crustacea, the copepods and krill.

There is still another group of temporary animal plankton

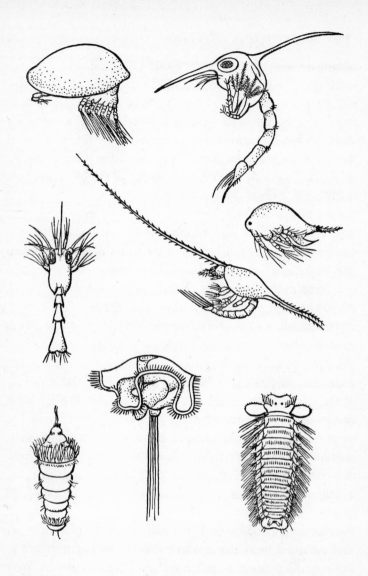

*Figure 6.* Temporary animal plankton. Barnacle, crab and other shell fish larvae (above) and sea worm larvae (below).

which in turn has an intimate and important relationship with the fishes. Cod, halibut and flatfish, such as plaice, feed on the bottom of the sea and are dependent for food upon worms, small bivalves, sea-snails and crustacea. Many of these bottom-living creatures release their eggs or have free-swimming larvae which drift aimlessly in the plankton until, in turn, they grow large enough to settle again to the bottom as adults. In the plankton stage they also provide food for young fishes that prey upon that sort of diet. We shall discuss the plankton in detail as a food for man in a later chapter, but here our concern is its part in the complex internal economy of the sea.

The ocean environment has several distinct advantages for the growth of vegetation over that of the land. On land plant life has to adjust to soil, the atmosphere and sudden and drastic changes of moisture and temperature, but plankton plants float in a beneficent bath of water which chemically is in close affinity to their own fluids, which supports them easily without the necessity of strong skeletons and which acts at one time both as soil and air and as a guard against climatic vagaries. Water is the most efficient solvent for the raw materials necessary for plant growth; it is slow to change in temperature and tends to resist, as a buffer solution, sudden changes either acid or alkaline. Sea water, in fact, is the most appropriate environment for the living cell. In the sea there are no arid deserts although there are a few relatively barren areas. Nutriments course both up and down through the circulating bath that protects and supports life. So, to the advantage of sea life there is a relative uniformity of environment, simple and constant, in time as well as in space, within the medium of the salt sea. Marine creatures do not have to adapt to sudden shifts of moisture, temperature or the violent assault of the elements and this requires of them a much simpler task in adjusting to the environment.

There are, of course, handicaps caused by this uniformity of environment. Plankton is at the mercy of many factors that modify its wide distribution. For one thing, the temperature and saltiness of the water, although remarkably constant from time to time in comparison with land, does change somewhat from place to place and from depth to depth. When change does occur it has a bad effect. The simple requirements of the normal sea environment have not, as on land, bred much range of adjustability. Also, the water currents which can bring food to the semi-helpless plankton can also sweep them away from a favorable or optimum environment. All of these factors play a part in the fluctuating growth of the great ocean meadows but none of them a more important part than the supply of fertilizer.

We have already looked at the hazards of the fertilizer cycle for land plants. A great part of land fertilizers, after application, finds its way eventually into the sea. Thus the oceans are, in a sense, giant hydroponic systems with the plankton vegetation constantly bathed in fertilizer, though in a very dilute solution. It is interesting to consider what happens to this fertilizer and how this vital supply, itself fluctuating, determines the great variation in the final yield of the plankton crop.

Just as the fertilizer released by the decay of natural vegetation on land returns to the soil, so does the fertilizer released from vegetable plankton return to the sea. Also, when the animal plankton or the fishes die and decay, chemical change and the action of bacteria release fertilizers to the sea water. But beyond this initial similarity there is a most important difference. The shallow land soil, only inches deep, holds for immediate use the rich decayed vegetable matter of humus. But in the ocean, which has an average depth of two and a half miles, the phosphorus and nitrogen compounds tend to leave the upper layers of the sea where plants can grow and instead are carried by certain processes to deep water, where they are no longer immediately available.

As the rich and short-lived vegetation in the sunny areas beneath the waves decays it sifts slowly down upon the dark floor of the sea along with the minute animals that graze these pastures, and with them are carried the incorporated fertilizing elements that first gave them life. The final result of decay is to release the fertilizer to the water but by the time this happens, the dead bodies and the fertilizer have reached ever greater depths. Where the waters are shallow, the natural turbulence of the sea controlled by the seasons of the storm or calm returns this nutriment at various intervals to the surface pastures, but this variability of supply, in relation to seasonal changes of temperature and sunlight and the grazing action of the animal plankton, naturally causes a tremendous fluctuation in growth. Thus, just as on the land, the underwater world of the ocean has its seasons with alternations of bumper crops or of crop failure. On land we have devised ways of combating this fluctuation of seasonal conditions but in the sea as yet we have no real control or powers of interference with the wild rhythm of nature.

On land man lives and breathes in the same environment as the plants and animals upon which he depends for his life and the changing effects of the seasons are obvious and visible to us from the changes in the forests, the flight of migrating birds and the green army of the grasses marching north each spring. We know when to plant and when to harvest and when to fertilize and irrigate and even spray against enemies of the crops. But under the sea the almost invisible pasturage of algae and plankton is beyond our observation or help, as it adjusts to the seasonal shifts and changes of its salt environment.

Temperature and light are the common controlling factors of the oceanic seasons. The power of a plant to grow and use the ever-present fertilizers in the sea is of course controlled by photosynthesis and this rate of growth increases with temperature. In fact, most biological activity doubles with a 10° Centigrade rise in temperature. So in the temperate latitudes, with the advent of winter cold, there is a widespread slowing down of plant growth within the sea. The plants of the plankton, whose life span is measured by a few days, either manage to reproduce themselves sufficiently to sustain a minimum population or else they produce resting spores and go into a sort of hibernation.

But as the sun becomes more powerful with the spring, and its life-giving rays penetrate deeper beneath the sea and as the temperature of the waters increases, a sudden and rapid growth commences in the plankton world just as the vegetation of the land returns to life. This invisible ocean outburst is swift and widespread and sometimes happens at such a pace that it discolors the waters of the shallower seas which almost choke with a glut of millions of minute cells. Spring storms and tides and currents catch and recirculate the constant loss of fertilizer from this teeming recurrent cycle of life and keep the surface waters rich in nutriment. This great vegetable blooming brings on a like increase in the animal plankton feeding on the growing tide of vegetation, until replacement is difficult. With summer the calmer weather reduces the turbulence of the waters and so prevents the free circulation of fertilizers. The added warmth of the sun also makes the surface water less dense so that it mixes less easily with the layers beneath. This double effect slows down water movement and mixing and so interferes with the normal rejuvenation of the grazing pastures of the surface. Nutriment ceases to return constantly to the sunny upper levels where the vegetation flourishes. This, plus the continued inroads of the animal plankton, results in overgrazing of the sea pasturage and the vegetable crop is curtailed.

When the autumn seasonal change in weather sets in there is, however, a second less ebullient season of growth for the sea meadows. The drop in temperature equalizes the water densities and the autumn winds and waves now act effectively to re-create the necessary mixing of the layers of the sea and fertilizer again comes to the sunny surface. This works just as when we rejuvenate soil by plowing it and bringing the lower layers to the surface. Also the grazing animal plankton have been reduced in number because the minute fish-fry and the offspring of bottom animals have begun to mature and to seek other pastures. For a short while under this reduced grazing the vegetable plankton increases, but, with the advent of winter, the restraint of colder temperatures and milder sun cuts them down to a minimum. The ocean year has ended.

This is a simplified account of the effects of the complicated interaction of fertilizer, temperature and light and grazing upon the wide meadows and pastures of vegetable plankton that spread along the borders of the shelving continents. Further offshore in the deep waters the continual rain of microscopic plant and animal remains; settling on the remote ocean floors would remove all fertilizer from the surface waters if there were not also a mechanism for the return of rich bottom waters upward to the reaches of the sun. This is accomplished by great currents both horizontal and vertical, such as the Gulf Stream and the upwelling of waters off Africa and the western shores of South America. The sun indirectly causes this great hydroponic pump to function by creating the differences in temperature that stir these currents directly through heat energy and indirectly through the winds brought about by atmospheric convection. The energy of heat translated into motion sustains the fertile cycle of oceanic life.

The floating helpless-seeming life of the oceans not only drifts with the currents but also exists partly by taking advantage of a current of nutriment which continuously is pumped upward from the sterile dark of the abyss to the life-giving areas of the sunlight. These strong upwellings of water occur where currents diverge or where, as off the western coast of Africa, the constant offshore winds push water from the land which has to be replaced from below, bringing with it the rich fertilizer of the deep waters. Thus, variations of temperature indirectly govern the distribution and growth of the plankton by water movement in the open sea and, in addition, directly control the kinds and seasons of the plankton. A relatively small rise in temperature greatly increases the metabolism of the microscopic life enabling it to take fuller advantage of the upward rain of nourishment riding the currents. The food chain is established that supports the small fishes that are eaten by the bigger fishes that are eaten by man. The rising water movements give continuity to this everlasting supply of fertilizers which sustain the pastures of the sea without help of man. The problem of fluctuating crops in the sea, though analogous to that of the land, is a complicated process and the ocean economy starting from the invisible life is a more complex one. On land we have a simple chain of fertilizer, vegetable, and herbivore working under conditions which are, within limitations of climate, susceptible to the artificial control of man through agriculture and animal husbandry. In the ocean, with a much more lengthy and complicated food chain, many more factors exist which affect crop yields. From the wide base of the myriad plankton, with each succeeding step in size and availability to man there is a loss of quantity. Just as it takes ten tons of vegetation to make one ton of beef so there is at sea a great diminution of yield at each of the several stages of the ocean feeding chain. The fish production is less than one-tenth of 1 per cent of the total plant production in the sea. Yet fish is today our principal source of food from the sea and so we shall consider it first.

In thus briefly sketching the cycle of life within the salt biosphere of the oceans we have dealt in simplified fashion with the complex biological, chemical and physical cycles which control food production. Now we can consider the potential yield of the great sea fisheries which form the peak of the food pyramid and assess the problems and difficulties of the special conditions which stand between mankind and the full use of this rich storehouse of energy.

# CHAPTER 3

## The Fish and the Fisherman

THE FOOD THAT MAN LIVES BY IS roughly divided into carbohydrates and protein. The former give us ready energy and the proteins are the body builders. Potatoes and good red meat are their familiar examples. Our most available carbohydrates are vegetables and they may be produced from a given area of ground in about a ten to one ratio over meat proteins. Thus one of our greatest difficulties in the face of a rapidly growing world population is to make more protein available to mankind. That is why our curiosity naturally turns to the oceans where 90 per cent of the world's possible food material is produced by nature. Fish is a concentrated protein diet with the advantage over some forms of protein produced on land that it contains all of the amino acids which are essential to our diet. In other words, under the sea is a vast ill-harvested and largely unexplored resource of food that is at least the equal, if not superior, in nourishment to the finest meats we can raise on land. Taking a world average of normal prices the fisherman receives a lower price for bulk fish delivered at the dock than does the cattleman for bulk meats off the range. It is obvious the world had better go fishing seriously.

Science, in analyzing the delicate chemistry of our bodies and their daily needs, has discovered that not only are certain calory-producing foods necessary to us but that they must be combined with other less obvious sources of energy and growth such as vitamins, mineral elements and oligoelements, all of which have been found in fish and seafoods in general in sufficient quantity to make them a well-balanced diet for man. The additional presence of fat in fish provides energy and the vitamins A, D and the B complex are equally essential. Recent experiments at Harvard, especially as to vitamin A from fish livers, suggest that these natural vitamins may have beneficent properties that are lacking in the synthetic product. This simply means that fish is a well-rounded and natural food admirably suited as to quality for the task of solving present or future food shortages.

There are other advantages to fish as a primary diet for mankind. Much-needed minerals such as phosphorus, calcium, potassium and magnesium are found in the flesh of fishes together with adequate quantities of iodine, iron, and copper. This sounds rather mechanical but we can keep in mind that fresh fish is not only a delicious food if handled with reasonable skill but one of the most digestible forms of protein and quite as stimulating, pound for pound, as beef and, in most cases, a little kinder to the family budget. This is due to the fact that it takes only half the man hours of labor to deliver fish to the dock, weight for weight that it does to raise and tend and deliver beef to the slaughter houses. This being so, we must naturally ask ourselves why we are not taking greater advantage of this ocean resource, since the world catch under present conditions falls short of supplying the world's deficit in protein requirements.

The Food and Agricultural Organization of the United Nations has made a careful world-wide study of the problem of food supply for the leaping populations of modern times. In the first place it has discovered that the world consumption of meat at 50 million tons per annum is far from enough for the normal requirements. In fact, as much as two-thirds of the people on the face of the earth are failing to get the minimum protein requirements for a healthy body and mind. It would be necessary at once to increase meat production by 13 million tons merely to correct this want and by another 30 million tons to reach the minimum requirements of the world population in 1960, just a few short years ahead of us. This obviously can not be done, or probably even approximated, by any means available to us from presently developed agricultural areas or under the price arrangements that also inevitably govern production. So the question of catching fish becomes daily more important.

It has become increasingly clear that the question of fish resources as a remedy for present protein food shortages is not merely a count of fish in the sea and the organization of fleets to bring them in. The fish are there but they move and scatter and insist on living in areas so far from the hungry mouths on shore that it is beyond the means of a competitive economy to go and fetch them. It is not likely that using present methods we will come anywhere near making up the world protein deficit from the wealth of the sea although that wealth is there awaiting man's ingenuity to harvest it. Today, as things actually stand, we only harvest 20 million tons of fish annually for our use. This is a gross tonnage from which we must deduct waste and offal and the catch of fish like menhaden which are used for fertilizers. The net available fish for our table as food protein amounts to about one million tons, i.e., one-thirteenth of the immediate world requirements and only one-thirtieth of what we will need five years from now to merely catch up with a minimum world demand. Lumping the good and bad pastures of the sea together, this averages less than one pound per acre. Even for a hunting society, that is not much to brag about.

Although the problem of getting more help from the sea for hungry man demands an active exploration for new fishing grounds, there also exists the problem of more efficient and economic harvesting of the grounds and areas which we now know to be prolific. As far as the abstract problem goes, the theoretical potential yield could be very high indeed. We already have learned that the oceanic pastures produce about nine-tenths of of the world's vegetation. Even if we allow for a possible weight-loss ratio in the conversion of plankton to fish of a thousand to one, compared to the shorter and more efficient cycle of ten to one from grass to beef, still the total growth of fish in the oceans is vastly greater in amount than the present supply of meat on land. The food is there, scattered, difficult to find and reap and often far from market. Those are the kinds of handicaps that face modern exploitation of the rich mines of the sea.

We do not have to fall back on mathematical calculations to find evidence of this huge unknown supply of nourishment beneath the waves. In the next chapter we will discuss new electronic devices which have helped to locate fish in quantity existing in depths and places heretofore not considered apt for commercial fishing. But there are more obvious evidences of vast uncounted quantities of fish existing far from the continental shelf and the offshore banks which we now know of as fishing grounds. The Pribiloff Islands off Alaska each summer are host to some three million fur seals which migrate there annually from the southern Pacific waters. These seals are protected under international agreement on the breeding grounds. They are voracious feeders on types of fishes that could be useful to mankind. It has been estimated by oceanographers that each year a multitude of seals sweeping up and down the Pacific waters consumes one and a half million tons of fish and squid. This is actually more than the entire yield of the North Pacific fisheries of the United States and occasions no appreciable diminution in the overall supply of fish, as they are taken in the deep seas where man as yet does not compete.

A similar computation of fish consumption over and above that taken by man can be made from the guano production of the millions of cormorants that live on the islands west of Peru. This, too, indicates what a small fraction of the available supply of deep-water fish man has yet tapped for his own needs. A single flock of these sea birds on the Chincha Islands has been estimated at 700,000. It consumes alone as much fish, according to R. E. Coker, as a quarter of the entire commercial catch of the United States of America. A valuable by-product of this immense appetite of the cormorants is about 100,000 tons of dried guano or bird manure deposited here each year. So far this is the most effective way we have found for recovering some of the fertilizer that continually leaches away from the land and is washed into the sea and in part enters into the food chain of the fishes. These examples of the seals and the birds readily dramatize the turnover of available life under the sea. Similar if less striking examples of the great quantity of fish in the sea may be found all over the world.

In 1949 the United Nations Scientific Conference on the Conservation and Utilization of Resources brought together experts from many countries. Among other things, they made a map of possible areas of the oceans where new fisheries might be developed as well as making a careful study of present fishing grounds in relation to their full exploitation. It was generally agreed that, compared to the agricultural development of land, the fisheries of the world were open to a much greater expansion. For the moment we can leave aside the reasons why this expansion has not yet already occurred and see what the map of existing fishing grounds shows us. In the first place, 98 per cent of the world's commercial fishing is carried on in the Northern Hemisphere. There are various reasons for this, largely related to the unequal concentration of population and fishing effort, but also concerned with the geographical arrangements of shoals and currents and temperatures and the other factors which go to make up good grounds and feeding places.

Of the total catch of fish, Asia accounts for about half and the rest is divided: 32 per cent Europe, 16 per cent North America. Only 2 per cent is in the Southern Hemisphere. The oceans are fished as follows: Pacific 48 per

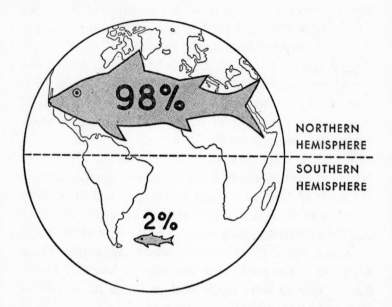

*Figure 7.* Distribution of world fish catches between northern and southern hemispheres.

cent, Atlantic 47 per cent and the Indian Ocean 5 per cent. The fishes which for the most part support these fisheries are few in number, and for convenience may be grouped as the cods, herrings, mackerels and shellfishes. In the shallow waters of the continental shelf, such as in the North Sea, a certain amount of flatfishes is caught by trawlers. In fact it may be said that out of about 20,000 known species of seafishes no more than fifty contribute to the bulk of our catch.

The North Sea is a good example of an area which is fished close to its limit of production. With the exception of herring, there was no increase in the output of North Sea fish between 1913 and 1932 in spite of a great advance in expensive modern equipment. As a result, much of the English fishing fleet now has to go far afield to Iceland and Greenland waters. This search for grounds distant from the old accustomed banks will have to go on. Methods of preservation and transportation must be evolved to make fishing economically feasible if our fish production is to be expanded on a sufficient scale. As an example, the United Nations experts generally agreed that new grounds for cod lay north of Norway towards Spitsbergen and in Alaskan waters, and for tuna and pilchards off the coasts of Africa and South America, with trawling banks west of the bulge of Africa where rising currents enrich the waters. These are some of the possibilities awaiting the so-called know-how of man to solve mechanical problems in relation to costs and profits while the hungry wait.

It is a good idea here to make a brief analysis of our present inadequate sources of edible fish and the extent of the take in order to understand the reasons for our failure in the face of the extraordinary advances of scientific technology which have taken place in other fields over the past fifty years. The possibilities for great improvement are present but the difficulties are many. Let us first consider the most likely sources of a new fish crop and then the means of catching it.

The cold and temperate waters of the Northern Hemisphere produce the present bulk of the world fish supply for our consumption. In these northern waters, particularly in the Atlantic, are the famous fishing banks of the continental shelves which extend far out from our shores. In depths rarely exceeding 100 to 200 fathoms, two principal types of fishes are caught. The first of these are the bottom-living fishes which belong mostly to the cod family and include the cod's relatives, such as hake and haddock, and to the pleuronectids, which are flatfish such as sole, plaice, flounders and halibut. The second type are the surface-living fishes which include the herring and its relatives, the menhaden, sardines and pilchards; the salmon; and the mackerels, which include tunas.

The surface fishes spend a great part of their lives in the upper waters of the seas and usually have periodical migrations along well-defined routes, sometimes over great distances, although, as in the case of the tunas, we do not yet know in all cases the full round of their annual travels to and from their secret breeding grounds. Because of the seasonal appearance of these fishes the time for catching them in our northern waters is rather short and this introduces the difficulty of maintaining proper equipment for their pursuit during long periods of the year when they can be of no economic use. This naturally affects the labor factor also. The bottom fisheries are more constant because of shorter migrations of the fish and trawlers can work on more or less of a year-round schedule.

Because the bottom fishes do not roam beyond the reach of man in their periodic migrations, many of our northern fisheries, such as those for plaice and cod, are already fished to their highest point of production and, as in the North Sea, may even be overfished. As yet the Grand Banks of Newfoundland have not been overfished and there are indications that the cod fisheries can even be stepped up there and the catch of plaice or rough dab can be advanced. It is true that there seems to be a diminution of cod in the Gulf of Maine in recent years but this probably can be laid to the increasing warmth of the water rather than to excessive fishing.

In the Pacific the northern cod both in the Gulf of Alaska and the Bering Sea have yet to be fully utilized, while the prolific herrings which give by far the greatest yield of any known type of fish—some seven and a half billion are caught each year in the North Sea alone—are on the whole unexploited in the north Pacific waters. If the demand and price were right, this catch could be stepped up immeasurably. Also, in the Bering Sea there is a great area of 600,000 square miles where the yellow-tailed flounder is plentiful. Little accurate information comes through from the Russian fisheries in northern waters but it is believed that the Murman Sea is a good ground for a greatly increased catch.

In order to make full use of the available fish crop it is necessary to understand and predict the years of glut and of scarcity and to know what machinery of nature brings them about. Let us look at the cod. Since men first took to sea in the Atlantic it has been a familiar symbol of deep sea fishing as the landsman knows it. From the days of Columbus, Cartier and Cabot a fleet has fished the dangerous Grand Banks and the Icelandic waters, composed of vessels from France, Portugal and England and her American colonies. The cod is an old friend to the Atlantic peoples and in earlier days when meat was scarce, it was one of the main European staples of food. The cod is our familiar. He is taken more or less at 40 fathoms the year around but is at his best from January to March at the spawning grounds. These are southwest of Iceland, by the Lofoten Islands of northern Norway and in certain waters of the North Sea. A single female cod will shed between four and six million eggs in a season. Only two of these eggs need survive to maturity to keep the race of codfish in being, so that the enormous breeding potential is balanced by colossal infant mortality. As the eggs develop they float to the surface and are part of the plankton destined to be eaten by other fish and by their own kind. It is curious to note that when these eggs first develop into minute fishes perhaps an inch long they often seek shelter within the umbrella-like skirts of giant jellyfish where larger fish cannot catch them.

Shortly after this stage the small fry settle to the bottom where they carry on as best they can with their larger relatives although they tend to keep pretty well inshore in shallow waters where they grow slowly to about three inches in their first year. They attain their best growth and are in the best shape for market by their fifth or sixth year but can live to twenty. In passing, it is interesting to note that the present increase in temperature in northern waters, particularly around Greenland, has moved cod fishing together with other sorts far up along the western shores of Greenland. In the past thirty years there has been a marked rise in temperature of the sea around Spitsbergen. The result has been a northward extension of cod grounds into areas of sea previously too cold. Whether this change in ocean temperature that has continued more or less steadily since the 1920's is temporary or will be of long standing is anybody's guess, but the Danes and, in fact, all European fishermen are at present exploiting this rich new source. A few figures will illustrate this change. Tons of fish caught in Greenland follow: In 1911: 18; in 1925: 1000; in 1930:

8160; in 1940: 7000; in 1945: 12500 and in 1947: 14900. An even greater proportionate increase has been recorded in the arctic waters of the Barents Sea and the Murman coast north of Norway.

The question still remains of how to exploit to the full the seemingly inexhaustible supply of fish like the cod and there are many reasons why the cold water fisheries of the world have not been fully utilized and some of the Southern Hemisphere not even touched. In the end it often boils down to a matter of economics. The fishing grounds are at great distances from the centers of marketing and of population and it takes time to haul heavy-laden craft through stormy seas carrying not only fish but fuel and the means of refrigerating them. This tends to limit the greatest fishing efforts to areas like the North Sea or the Grand Banks which are reasonably near the home market. One cannot escape the simple economic factor that the energy and manpower and capital expended to produce food and transport it to the consumer must be in a reasonably low proportion to the energy value of the food itself. Unless of course artificial subsidies are applied.

On the whole, except for localized areas such as the North Sea grounds, which have been more and more intensively fished for several centuries, man has had little to do with the periodic fluctuations of good and bad years of fishing except as market demand has increased or decreased the fishing effort. Nature itself provides long- and short-term rhythms of fertility beneath the waters of the sea that are becoming less chancy and mysterious to man as the science of oceanography develops. But this has not always been so well understood. In the old days, during the bad years in Norway when the cod, and in particular the herring, fell off in their annual visits to those northern waters, the ill luck would like as not be blamed on some moral insufficiency in the people and regarded as a just punishment for sin. Science, here at least, is gradually supplanting medieval superstition and its successor, the blind modern belief that conservation must mean restriction. There are various good reasons for a glut or lack of fish in the seas, irrespective of the splendid productivity of the females who cast their millions of eggs into the waters or of the males who in a generalized sort of sexual fervor cast their sperm abroad haphazard. What eventually happens to the reproductive fruit of any particular year, for the most part, seems to depend on the early days of the maturity of the egg and larvae under conditions of current and temperature and predator beyond the control of fish or man.

Man became aware of the importance of these individual year groups or classes by noting the successive ebb and flow of the fish populations. In the North Sea for the past four hundred years this vital supply of food has been under close observation and history seems to show a general tendency for the herring to run in good number for a period of fifty to eighty years, followed by poor catches for a period of thirty to sixty years. The fluctuation of the fishing has probably followed, as far as we now can tell, changes in climate and water temperature and shifting layers of ocean currents that bring or withhold the plankton upon which the herring feed. In a word, the science of a reasonably accurate prediction of the sea's wealth and its whereabouts goes back to a developed research covering oceanography and the long-term influences of meteorology. It is as if our farm lands represented the plankton pastures but were in their fertility subject to an additional and complicated fluctuation from year to year covering wide geographical areas, and governed by winds and wild predators beyond our control.

So current, temperature and the fight for food are basically the cause of fluctuations in good or bad fish crops and these fish crops are not immediately determined but depend on the fate of the individual year classes. Perhaps the actual egg count is not very important because so few eggs need mature to guarantee adequate supply. What really counts is the optimum conditions of growth for the larvae and small fry, plenty of the right kind of plankton food and not too much storm and predator and a normal flow of waters and temperatures helpful to planktonic growth when the young fish are starting out on their dangerous venture to survive. As a matter of fact, if the majority of fish eggs were not destroyed, the sea would soon overflow with fish. The eggs and the small fry are an important part of the diet of the survivors as they mature just as the minute almost invisible vegetable plankton are necessary pasturage for the small fry while they await their turn to be eaten. There is a terrific concentration of numbers into size in the fish that come to table.

But we need not have many years of good survival—that is, good year classes—to keep the supply of fish at the maximum. The young produced in these few successful years are sufficient in number to surmount the great losses due to the voracious appetite of their elders and to become eventually part of the commercial catch. They are available for man during the several years of their maturity in the case of many species, so that in this way one good brood year effects several years of supply to mankind. This brings it down to a careful study of young fish and their conditions for survival in order to predict good years on the banks for the fisherman some several years ahead of the time when the good classes graduate to our dinner tables. When science and industry combine to chart the young fish crop year by year it will be possible to adjust the catch to prevent wastage in the big years or useless economic expenditure in readied equipment in the lean years.

Earlier in this book we spoke of fishing as still more or less in the hunting stage of development in relation to the much more advanced practice of agriculture. The nature of the seas, of course, is a partial answer but does not account for all the lag. The really very narrow limits of our fisheries are also influenced by the nature of our land migrations and the convenient centers of population which furnish a ready market. But there is no excuse, with our modern advances in techniques, refrigeration and speed of transport, for not greatly extending the areas of catch under intelligent economic management and the aid of government or institutional research. To recapitulate: 98 per cent of our fish are caught in the Northern Hemisphere and most of this north of the Tropic of Cancer. And this in view of the fact that only 60 per cent of the Northern Hemisphere is sea in comparison to 80 per cent of the Southern.

But, in a way, it is this very proportion of excessive water area to land area which limits the coastal banks, plus the lack of population concentration along the seaboards near the good fishing that helps keep down the industry in the Southern Hemisphere. Also, there are fewer good shallow banks for trawling in the southern waters where, as in South America, the continental shelf drops off steeply.

Another vital factor is the presence of well-defined circulation systems in relation to the fertilizer supply in bottom waters. The Atlantic Ocean has the system of the Gulf Stream and the North Atlantic Current and Canaries Current; the sinking of waters off Labrador and Greenland and the mouth of the Mediterranean; the beneficial mixing of Gulf Stream and polar waters and the slow rise of deep waters elsewhere. As we wrote of these movements in *The Ocean River*: "The Ocean River, with its branches and its tributary streams, acts like a gigantic pump, continually replenishing the depleted fertilizer (consumed by plankton) in this natural hydroponic system from the deep sea reservoir. Wherever surface water is blown by the winds away from the land, or where it streams apart in diverging currents, the underlying cold water, with its rich store of chemical food, is drawn up to replace it. The west coast of South Africa is a notable example of such a place—and here is a major fishery. The seas off the west coast of Portugal and Morocco are likewise areas of upwelling waters that provide the nutrition for tuna and sardine fisheries. In the Gulf of Mexico the major fishing area of the Campeche Banks is also an area of divergent water flow."

The Pacific Ocean, with a system of stronger currents than the South Atlantic, has areas still needing exploration and development where there are considerable quantities of surface-living fishes such as the tunas, mackerels and, in some areas, sardines. Such areas as that stretching from Indonesia to the Dutch East Indies are reported to be potential grounds for yellow-fin tuna fisheries. Also Australian grounds and the upwelling currents off Chile and Peru offer areas of much greater potential than we have yet realized and vast quantities of anchovies and pilchards are believed to lie off the Atlantic coasts of Brazil. But still, compared to the colder waters of the sea, the warm areas are believed to offer more limited possibilities.

In the complicated pyramid of fertility that leads to the food energy readily available to man in the captured fish, the basic factor is the distribution of fertilizers, just as on land. The nutritious fertilizing salts which sustain the plankton pastures where the fish graze are concentrated in the surface waters in the neighborhood of the continental masses over the submerged continental shelves. The death and decay of life in the sea, slowly sinking to the ocean bottoms, transfers this fertilizing element away from the sunny surface waters. The cold currents and the winter cooling of the seas, causing the water to become heavier, hasten the mixing. This causes a new transfer of bottom and waters to the surface and so keeps the supply of fertilizer circulating in reach of the plankton which feed upon it. In the more uniformly warm tropical waters there is not enough seasonal differentiation in temperature to bring about strong vertical movement and so the mixing process is hindered, less fertilizer returns to the surface and hence less plankton and less fish. Where fertility is low it naturally follows that fishing is poor.

But if we go far enough south toward the seas where the cold waters of the Antarctic fringe the polar continent, there is an upwelling of fertile deeper waters and it is here that the "krill" or animal plankton in the form of small shrimplike creatures is so thick that it easily feeds the giant bodies of whales each of which scoop in a ton a day of this food. In spite of this obviously fertile sea, no large fishery based upon surface-living fishes has as yet been developed and the waters are too deep to allow of bottom fishing. Probably few bottom fish live there. It is possible, though, that commercially useful fishes may be eventually exploited here in quantity. Perhaps pelagic migratory schools may be found at some distance below the surface waters. Similar divergent currents also occur in the Pacific along the equatorial belt where bottom nutrients are pumped to the surface and here potential fisheries are even today being found.

We have gone into the nature of the factors controlling potential harvests of the vast ocean resources of fish because it is easy to think that all man has to do is to apply know-how and the supply of protein from the oceans can be stepped up many times the present catch. It is there, isn't it? The actual opinion of the world fishery experts assembled at the United Nations Conference was that it might be increased around 22 per cent by finding new grounds and by further exploitation of areas already used. This careful and reasoned estimate has taken into consideration all the various handicaps that extend from the sea to the housewife's market basket. Some of the difficulties are technical, some geographical and some a matter of economics, due to concentration of population not necessarily gibing with concentrations of fish. And of course people themselves are ultraconservative in their eating habits and hard to educate to new ways.

It has been estimated that on some fishing grounds half of the catch is thrown away as trash which otherwise might in a great measure be used as food or fertilizer under more modern methods and attitudes. Many of the smaller fishes caught with the market fishes are perfectly palatable but they are strange and the housewife can't be bothered. Perhaps a third of the catch of some of our shore fisheries could thus be utilized instead of destroyed. This same waste occurs in fish viscera which are high in nutrition if manufactured into supplements for poultry and hog food. Here is a fresh field for more enterprise provided, of course, that the collection and concentration of a steady supply would justify the commercial investment. But if advantage were taken of all present techniques and information and if the economic and marketing problems were solved, it looks as if an estimate of double our present resources from fishing would not appear to be too optimistic.

Let us re-examine the question of production in the light of scientific estimates. The researches of Riley, Richey, Redfield, Clarke and others in the United States, together with Harvey in England, give us some idea of the total vegetable plankton growth in the sea. A rough estimate based on measurements shows this growth to vary from half a ton to ten tons per acre with an average yield of about three tons of dry plankton per acre. Taking into consideration the large quantity of plankton consumed by individual fishes and allowing for the losses at each stage of this food chain, it is fairly reasonable to assume that this tonnage of plankton will produce an oceanwide average end-product of about three one-hundreths of a ton of wet fish, or 20 pounds per acre.

Still remaining in the clear realm of statistics—since the oceans cover an area of 90 billion acres—the total production of fish in the seas of the world should be something in the order of one billion tons each year. This is over 30 times our present world catch. It would seem then that we should easily be able to foresee an increase of far more than double our present catch as it stands today. The chief reasons we cannot, lie in the deficiencies of our present-day methods of fishing and the uneven distribution and concentration of mankind and of the fishes themselves; in other words, the difficulties of technology, engineering and economics.

So far we have looked at the future expansion of the fish catch in the light of the distribution of the fishes themselves and with the limitations of the existing methods of fishing and the accustomed gear. We have not speculated on radical new developments which could bring about vastly increased efficiency. One of the chief problems in expanding the catch is to devise new methods to meet the unsolved problem of harvesting a thinly scattered crop, which is not always by nature concentrated in dense schools at conveniently located points, so that there is a profitable relationship between the fisherman's effort and his yield. As an example of the importance of dense schooling, it is interesting to note that of thousands of different kinds of fishes living in the sea, the herring types of fishes alone account for 15 per cent of the world production and the catch of codlike fishes (entirely in the Northern Hemisphere) is about the same. In the United States the sardine catch of California was formerly about a quarter of all the fish we took from the sea. Beyond the take of herring, cod, sardines and mackerel and a very few other species, the catch dwindles to very small proportions because of lack of concentration in commercial quantity.

This inspection of the future possibilities of the fishing

industries in the light of existing knowledge and methods alone indicates that production could well be doubled, at any rate greatly increased. We also see some obvious difficulties which lie across the path of any such progress. Most of these are economic rather than technological in nature. The well-fed peoples, with capital to develop increased and more widespread fisheries simply do not have the basic incentive to do so. Countries in which thousands die each day of starvation do not have the capital or technical skills or else they are remote from the undeveloped sea areas of potentially great fish production. The centers of human population were not established on the basis of fisheries and they do not coincide with such potential fishery areas as those of the South American coast. Even where conditions are more favorable to developing fisheries, the characteristic succession of glut and scarcity handicaps the individual investor. And, of course, our science of the sea is an infant one, our knowledge of the fishery resources, outside of a few of the major established ones, is small indeed. Before we can develop, we must be able to predict with reasonable accuracy. And before we can do this, we need far more basic research. This will help us to expand the offshore pelagic fisheries, where migrations are still much of a secret.

There is reason for hope that this wealth of seafood will not remain undeveloped. The Food and Agriculture Organization of the United Nations is helping to bring capital support to backward countries and to give technical assistance where fisheries are awaiting exploitation or development. There are organizations, such as the Gulf and Caribbean Fisheries Institute, which encourage the fishery scientist to recognize that the problem is not only one of biological research and technology but also one of economics and of politics. The infant sciences of oceanography are beginning to grow and follow in the footsteps of their great land counterpart in agriculture. They will certainly do much in the future, as ignorance gives way to understanding, to provide information which will lead to new sources of fish, new areas to develop and greater controls over the problems of fluctuating supply. But the full potentialities of the sea fisheries also await the services of technology and engineering to provide us with improved methods of finding, catching and transporting to market in good condition the fish which we know await them. Even as hunters, we have far to go in applying mechanical inventions and devices to the trapping of the rich protein sources of the ninety billion acres of ocean.

# CHAPTER 4

# The Ship and the Net

DUE TO THE NATURE OF THE OCEAN element, commercial fishing today is in essence not very different from the old times when the codfish fleet assembled in the sixteenth century off the Grand Banks. All over the world fish are still hooked, bagged or snared in refinements of primitive ways that man has known since the time of Homer and before. Today it is still net and line. To be sure, the lines may have a thousand hooks, the nets may hang for several miles across the tideways where the herring school, and the big trawlers may drag vast nets along the bottom for flatfish and haul them aboard with electric winches, but methods at sea have not reflected the great advance of agricultural practices on land. We can hope we are at the dawn of such an advance and that the hard study and coordinated research necessary for its accomplishment will be forthcoming.

The modern net may be fixed, as in the case of pound nets or weirs used for catching such fishes as salmon which tend to migrate along known paths and can therefore be

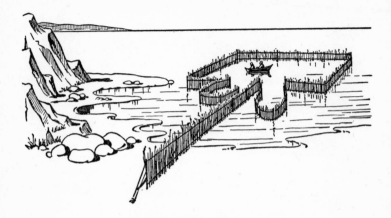

*Figure 8*. A typical fixed net. Maine herring weir at low tide.

guided into traps. This is, of course, limited to shallow waters, and this system of standing traps may be seen in various guises throughout the world. The movable nets dragged along the sea floor are known as trawls and these are used for the bottom fishes. Essentially they consist of conical bags of netting towed behind a vessel across the sea floor in order to sweep the fish into the path of the wide-open mouth. Originally such nets were held open by a rigid frame but today the mouth is extended by simply attaching glass or plastic floats to the upper edge and weights to the lower. These glass floats are familiar objects. Sometimes when torn loose by storm or rock, they are caught by the Gulf Stream and journey across the ocean from Portugal to our American shores. The corners of the mouth of the trawl are spread out by means of kitelike wooden boards, known as otter boards, attached to long

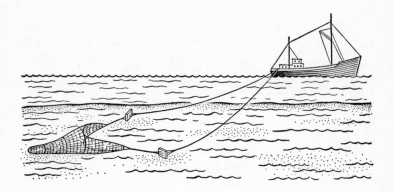

*Figure 9.* Otter trawl in operation.

cables and so angled that the water pressure drives them apart and keeps the net well spread. The cables of this gear, called Vigneron-Dahl after the inventors, which connect the net and the otter boards tend to frighten and thus herd the fish into the entrance of the net.

Surface fish, such as herring and mackerel, are caught in seines or wall nets, often several miles long, which are hung in the water supported by floats. Such a net drifts across the tide and the fish, not seeing it well, especially at night, plunge into its meshes and are caught by their gill covers when they struggle to free themselves. Other large surface nets, such as purse seines, are drawn in a circle around a school of fish and then drawn together. The bottom of the net is tightened like a string purse so that the fish cannot escape and are effectually bagged.

The hook and line methods are mostly used by small individual operators and in the old days by hand-fishers from

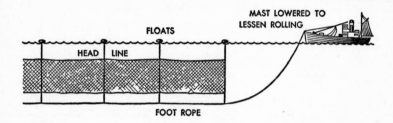

*Figure 10.* A drift net in operation. Fishes such as herring are caught in the meshes by their gills.

the codfishing schooners. Often, long lines with many hooks are anchored at one end and allowed to drift under floats with the shorter lines carrying the hooks dangling from the main line, baited with squid or whatever local practice may dictate.

Except for the addition of power and size to the vessels, remarkably little of a radical nature has been done to change the fishing in the past four hundred years. The Grand Banks are typical. It is amusing to read a report by Nicholas Denys, who went to the west from France in the mid-seventeenth century as a fisherman from the same small channel ports that still send out their vessels after cod. He says, in his *Natural History of North America*: "It is necessary that a captain who sets out from France for this fishery should make preparation for a provision for six months at least. After he is equipped, he sets sail and goes, by the Grace of God, to find the Grand Bank. Having arrived there, all sails are furled and the ship is prepared for the fishery. The tiller of the rudder is attached to one side, so the vessel remains almost as if she were at anchor, though she drifts nevertheless when there is a wind. Some now throw over their lines and others build a staging along one side of the vessel outside. Upon this staging are placed barrels; these are half hogsheads, which reach to the height of the waist. Each fisherman places himself inside his own. They also have a large leathern apron which extends from the neck to the knees placed outside the barrel in order to insure that the water, brought up by the lines, shall not run into the barrel. The lead (with hook) must not reach bottom by two fathoms. He catches a single cod at a time. A good fisherman is able to take as many as three hundred and fifty per day, but that greatly tires his arms. If they did this every day, they would not be able to stand it. There are ships that will be fortunate enough to complete their fishery in a month to six weeks, others will be there from three to five months."

Today, Diesel engines power the fishing schooners and the trips are shorter and ice replaces salt, but it is still a matter of hunting the prey and enduring the rigors of North Atlantic weather at its worst and foggiest. With the trawlers, the introduction of the otter boards and the Vigneron-Dahl cable-spreader for bottom fishing by net has done much to overcome the handicap of earlier more primitive trawling. There is hope that further modifications may increase the effective spread of the nets and in midwater-fishing open up possibilities for the future exploitation of hitherto unused types of fishes. In the case of the purse seine a great advance has been the use of pumps for removing the catch from the pursed-up net directly into the ship's hold, thus making it possible to speed up operations and avoid injury to the fish while shoveling them inboard.

It is obvious that these methods and their development are mostly applicable to fish in concentrated schools and in relatively shallow waters off our continental coasts where fishing has gone on from time immemorial. What we must look to are new and less conventional methods developed to catch the quantities of fish in deeper ocean waters and those that swim in a more scattered fashion in some areas of the continental shelf due to smaller schools or to the scattered sparse distribution of their food. This is largely a problem of engineering, and the United Nations Food and Agricultural Organization has been fostering interest in this and related problems of ship and net design in recent international conferences in Paris and Miami. In this country too, The Marine and Fisheries Engineering Institute of Woods Hole, Massachusetts is devoting itself primarily to similar types of research. So far no practical method has yet been evolved for the economic harvesting of widely scattered fish although they probably do exist in quantity in the offshore waters and there are plenty of concentrations of bank fishes too thin to handle economically.

Perhaps it is a question of Mahomet and the mountain. There are ways to make the fish come to the fisher, based on a knowledge of the natural biological behavior of the fish themselves. Light attracts animals and so does smell. We trap insects because they concentrate in the neighborhood of strong light. So do many fish, as can be observed anywhere along the Mediterranean as the local boats go out with strong night lanterns to net the scattered fish of those clear waters. Also in the United States many of us have enjoyed the sport of jacking for flounders and eels at half-tide along the mud flats of the eastern coasts. These fish naturally swim into the lighted area and can then be readily speared. The Japanese, picking up an old Javanese practice, have developed a lighting system for use with small fishing boats which go after the saury. The schools are attracted by strong electric lights to liftnets attached to bamboo poles and as the fish approach the boats, winches raise the net beneath the surfacing school. It is possible that in the future, means may be found to extend the practicability of this light lure to attract the scattered fishes of other types.

Many more radical developments may come from the other primitive method of the chemical bait or the baited hook which the fish can see and smell. There have been no important changes directly in the application of new or chemical types of bait although surely, with the great modern advances in biochemical knowledge, there must be possibilities awaiting development in this direction. But another attraction based on the behavior characteristics of fish has been discovered in the tendency of fish to react to electric fields in the water and to swim towards the anode or positive pole when placed in such a field. This has not been used as yet with any great success by sea fishermen but there is some promise that methods within the economic reach of market fishermen can yet be perfected and put into practice.

Work along these lines has been carried on both in Europe and the United States in recent years. Dr. Kreutzer in Germany initiated the first large-scale work several years ago. He established experimental pens and found that the

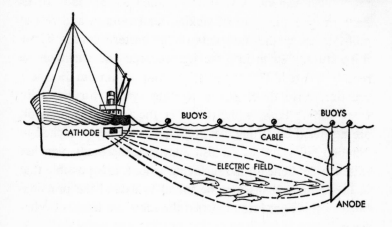

*Figure 11.* Diagram of the manner in which fish may experimentally be caused to move along the path of an electric field.

---

fish swim towards the positive pole of the electric field and if the current is strong enough can be stunned. In California and at Miami similar experiments for attracting sardines into nets have gone forward and from the laboratory standpoint have been successful.

An advantage of this method is that large fishes need relatively less electric current than small fishes so that the size of fish caught is controllable. Electric fishing has been tried in other ways. One way is to use an electrified hook to stun large fish, such as tunas. In another method described by the Soviet scientists, the fishes are electrically attracted to the mouth of a large pipe and are pumped into the ship's hold. It is not likely that such a device as this would have useful application except for the rapid loading of densely schooling fishes and there is no good evidence that it has been put to commercial use so far.

Electrical methods may be applied directly to the net itself where the net is made the anode or positive pole and the cathode as a cable is towed ahead of the net. The fish tend to move towards the anode and are attracted directly into the net and there stunned. This method might seem best for small fish and shrimp but the small size of these creatures has the paradoxical effect of requiring more current. At present it is being tested for the shrimp fisheries of the Gulf of Mexico at the Marine Laboratory of the University of Miami. Shrimp fishing is hazardous for the costly nets in many places because of rough bottom and coral reefs, so that any method that would attract the shrimp from this type of bottom into a midwater net would be of great value. The net would be towed above the rocky bottom clear of obstructions, with electrodes so arranged as to lure the shrimp upward into the mouth. In the case of larger fish, such as tuna, or even huge whales, it has been found possible to use electrified harpoons, electrified hooks or floating electrodes capable of stunning the prey. So far these have not come generally into use. Here, as in the development of all such apparatus, the final test must always be met—does it pay financially as well as bring improvement in the catch?

In spite of several years of attempts along these lines it cannot be said that electrical fishing has met the commercial test. One of the obvious problems is the necessity for creating a considerable amount of electric power aboard the fishing vessel. Another factor is that the amount of power increases at least as the square of the distance between the fish and the electrode. Even by using intermittent current this is still excessive. So, in spite of many enthusiastic predictions, the use of electricity for trapping great new catches of fish is nowhere near a present actuality. Perhaps some of the overoptimism along this line has been due to the success of electrical trapping methods in fresh waters. There is a need not only for the improvement of present methods of fishing through careful research and development but also for fresh thinking and experimentation and the application of entirely new techniques derived from advances in other fields of engineering. There is no reason to believe that the current trend towards development of new and interesting types of gear may not end in substantial improvement in the world fish catch.

No matter what improvements are made in the near future, the business of catching fish for the market is still largely a matter of hunting a scattered prey. Even fish already concentrated in schools may move rapidly about a large area of sea beyond the immediate sight of man. So not only is it important to improve the weapons we use, but the means of first locating the prey are also of the utmost importance. Much of the valuable time a vessel is at sea is still spent locating suitable schools and, also, part of the ship's function as a hunter is to locate new and suitable areas that have as yet not been discovered or exploited where large scale fishing can go on. This naturally makes new methods of discovering fish as important as developing more efficient methods to trap them, once located.

It was inevitable that the use we made of airplanes as submarine spotters would lead to the use of light planes for the searching out of schools of fish. This method is, of course, only suitable for the types of fishes that live near the surface of the sea and even in this capacity the airplane is limited by weather conditions and other handicaps not met with in vessels. But in spite of obvious handicaps it has, for example, been used by California tuna fishermen with success and has greatly helped in an experimental development of the basking-shark fishery in the Hebrides off the western coast of Scotland. This particular attempt to develop a fishery, started after the last war by the initiative of Gavin Maxwell, though small in scope and eventually abandoned, is worth a slight digression here because it so well illustrates the manifold difficulties of bringing to market resources that apparently lie ready at hand to exploit.

Here was a fresh problem to which old methods could be applied or new methods devised. Off the Island of Skye and among the outer Hebrides lie fishing grounds for herring and mackerel. The tides are swift, the seas subject to sudden storms roaring in from the wide Atlantic. There is fog and the fishing is often difficult. Added to this, large numbers of huge sharks, averaging more than 25 feet in length and weighing several tons, patrol the waters and do great damage to the nets.

Maxwell got the notion of catching these basking shark, so called from their habit of floating just at the surface of the sea, and of extracting oil from their livers, marketing the flesh as food and using their skins as leather. He knew that shark-liver oil was many times richer in vitamin A than cod-liver oil. On the Pacific coast of the United States at that time shark fisheries were selling liver oil at several hundred dollars a ton. Here in Scotland were huge sharks ready to hand. It looked like a good bet when he left the service after the war. He rigged a staunch fishing craft with derricks and winches and experimental harpoons and set forth. The story of his interesting persistent attempt to make this pay off can be found in his book *Harpoon At a Venture*. Many and varied problems of sighting, harpooning, hauling, delivering to a shore factory for processing and finally marketing these big sharks had to be met for the first time. Like many another fishing venture, it finally failed through the lack of adequate capital. But Maxwell's initiative cleared the way for new trials which, with greater efficiency in spotting the sharks by plane, using correct harpoons and more efficient processing, may well lead to future success.

Not only do new ventures in fisheries have to face untried methods of a technical nature, but the basic conservatism of fishermen, just as of farmers, brings further obstacles to surmount. But times are slowly changing. During the past few years the growing interest of scientists and engineers in the problems of catching fishes has resulted in many fresh attempts to adapt new ideas and devices to the industry. Among these is the use of television. It is now possible to enclose a compact television camera, of the type used for industrial purposes on land, into a watertight housing and to suspend this camera beneath the sea to a depth of several hundred feet. An image of the undersea world is reflected on the screen in the deckhouse of the controlling vessel. So far this device has been used largely for inspecting wrecks and other projects, and for the study of experimental fishing trawls in action in an effort to improve their catching ability. Although the instrument has not yet been perfected for the detection of deep schools of fish, there is some possibility that, combined with a self-contained light, it could serve as a fish finder.

But it is sound rather than sight which best permits man to reach with his extended senses down below the hitherto blank surface of the sea. The echo-sounding devices which were developed under the pressure of submarine war have since been put to peaceful uses. Although echo-sounding was fundamentally a navigational device to give a continuous reading of depth, it now can locate schools of fish. It is based on the fact that a sound impulse can be generated in a downward direction from a ship's hull and then, upon reaching the sea floor, be reflected like an echo back again to the source in the vessel where it is picked up by a hydrophone. The time required for the echo to return to the ship gives a measure of the changing depth of the sea. The actual construction of the instrument as used aboard ship makes it possible to convert the series of echoes into a continuous mark on a paper record, graduated in feet and meters or fathoms.

To the surprise of a few observant navigators, a false bottom echo or reflection of the sound impulse sometimes showed at a depth far less than the known true depth of the sea. This intermediate or false bottom sometimes was caused by fish and so it led to the use of the detector for locating schools in sufficient density to produce a strong echo. This is a vast improvement over the older methods of dragging a long line of piano wire and feeling for the impact of the fish in a school as they might bump against it. A skilled fisherman could often judge very accurately of a school by this method but the sonar impulse is a more accurate and reliable guide and can be used from a fast-moving vessel and the "false bottom" appearing on the chart shows when the ship is in the act of passing over an otherwise hidden school or even over large single individuals.

But the echo-sounder has its disadvantages because it only operates vertically below the vessel. A better device known as the echo-ranging gear was a later war development used for detecting submarines. It has a directional sound-head which can be operated on a swivel in various directions in a horizontal plane. Thus it is possible to discover the direction and distance from the ship of a school of fish near the surface. This instrument has only recently reached the market but it gives promise of great utility to fishermen in spite of certain disadvantages, such as the fact that temperature and the salinity of the water can deflect and disturb the direction of the sound-wave under certain conditions. This may yet prove out, however, as a most valuable device for all kinds of undersea exploring operations.

As research in these new and magic-seeming devices goes on, the same old problem comes up of working out the "bugs" or unforeseen difficulties that affect all new invention. Shrimp, for instance, do not reflect sound as well as some fishes since the degree or intensity of the echo depends at least in part on the difference in density between the object to be identified and the density of water. Fortunately, recent advances in research have developed electronic indicators that make it possible to detect echoes which are not recorded by the ordinary echo-depth meter. Research is being carried on at Woods Hole, Miami, and elsewhere to work out a practical solution for instruments capable of detecting shrimp and already at least one cathode-ray oscilloscope echo recorder has been placed on the market for the use of the fishermen.

There is another device for listening-in on what goes on beneath the sea, and this also is an application of a wartime gadget. Much to the surprise of the navy men who bent their ears in strained attention for submarine engines, other strange noises persisted in coming from the deeps beneath their vessels. They found out that many marine creatures make distinctive noises and doubtless communicate with each other. Whales and porpoises grunt and squeal, certain kinds of shrimp make loud snapping noises and various types of fishes make sounds which have been described by the astonished listeners as croaks, whines, thumps, knocks, groans, barks, clicks, and rasps. These communications or soundings-off among the fish are, however, the exception and for the most part the inhabitants of the sea go about their business with an inscrutable silence. Moreover, whatever sounds are made have to compete with the louder noise of a fishing vessel's engines and the hull interference with the water. It is also possible that there may yet be discovered types of sound made by fishes that are beyond the range of the human ear but which can be detected by sensitive electronic recorders and be used for future exploratory work. It is safe to predict that some of the devices such as we have described will play a large part in future explorations by fisheries and will do much to extend our fishing grounds and to increase the extent of our catch. Already, reports indicate the location of deep cod shoals by supersonic methods and their subsequent location by underwater camera, so that we can now be sure that cod exist at greater depths and in areas other than the shallow continental shelf. The Japanese, who before the last war controlled 38 percent of the total world fish catch, have extended their tuna fishing into the mid-Pacific with good results.

As an illustration of the necessity for coordinated action in fishery research, it is well here to point out that the investigations of marine biologists into the behavior and feeding habits of fishes have provided an indirect method for the discovery and subsequent catch of fishes by studying the distribution of organisms upon which the fishes feed. This may be done by observing the various stages of the complicated food chain from plankton to cod or tuna. In the case of herring and certain other fishes which feed directly upon plankton, the fish are often discovered by taking plankton samples from the sea and searching for concentrations of the pasturage, so to speak. Herring tend to concentrate when feeding in the areas where the small shrimplike copepods are plentiful and, conversely, they avoid areas where there is too large a concentration of the small plant cells known as diatoms. On the basis of this type of research, A. C. Hardy, working in the North Sea, was able to devise his invention called the "plankton indicator." This is a small torpedolike object carrying a gauze disk. As it is towed through the water behind a fishing vessel, the plankton is sieved out by the disk. This disk can then be removed and studied for the type of feed in any particular water and the captain can decide on the nature of the fishing ground without going through the long labor of casting and hauling nets on the mere chance of a good catch. The diatoms will appear as a green or black material on the gauze, while the copepods will show red or orange.

Unless new inventions and more radical changes step up the slow perfection of traditional methods of fishing, customary on the banks of the continental shelf, the most we can hope for in the near future would be at best to double the present world catch of fish. Much more than this is needed if man is really to use the wealth of the sea for his protein diet. Any great increase must come in the future from the discovery and development of new sources in the deeper waters beyond the continental shelf, as we pointed out in the preceding chapter. Heretofore, the offshore areas were considered as relatively barren of fishes and yet, according to indications from recent exploratory work by oceanographers, these deep water areas may support considerably more fish life than we are at present exploiting. The truth is that our knowledge of the ocean, its currents and upwellings and the plankton pastures—all that goes to maintain the fish population—is even today more generalized than specific. Our detailed knowledge of the basic oceanography and of the fisheries is mainly limited to parts of the relatively shallow submerged rim of the continents. The frontier lies now beyond in the deeper waters where the Japanese have already successfully pioneered, driven by the whip of a burgeoning population. Just prior to the last world war their total catch amounted to 16 billion pounds per annum compared to 4 billion for the United States.

An interesting instance of our partial knowledge is shown by our ignorance of information regarding the origin of the giant bluefin tunas which support an important European and Mediterranean fishery. In the western Atlantic each year a separate population of them is known to migrate north and east, following more or less the course of the Gulf

Stream from the south. They appear during the latter part of May in the Florida Straits. At this time they are several hundred pounds in weight. Then, successively, they appear off the New Jersey coast, then New England and finally, in August off the shores of Nova Scotia. By this time they are even larger, since they have been feeding on herring and mackerel during their northward migration. Then they disappear again. Nothing more is heard of them until the time when the next year's run is on in the Florida Straits and the Bahama Islands. The rare appearance of individual large tuna in the Caribbean and the path of migration through the Straits of Florida suggests that there may be a great pool of these giant fishes somewhere in the Caribbean although they are so rarely seen there. Here is one case where considerable numbers of very large fishes have escaped detection, although all the evidence points to their presence in the apparently rather barren open water of the Caribbean. Similar circumstances exist also in the eastern Atlantic, where there well might be a breeding area for tuna which at present is unknown to us.

Striking evidence of the existence of considerable amounts of sea life in the open ocean also comes from the echo-sounder. Modern types record echoes, not only from the bottom but even from quite small suspended objects. And a few years ago oceanographers began to be mystified by a "phantom bottom," an echo where no bottom should be. Whenever this strange echo showed on the moving paper strip of the sound recorder, it remained for hours at a time, no matter how far or how fast the ship steamed, so that, if it were a school of fish, it would be one of monstrous size. Moreover, it extended sometimes as much as 300 feet thick and was usually too faint to be the echo of a school of fish.

Biologists are working to solve the riddle of the scattering layer, as it is called. It appears in daytime deep down at anything from 900 to 2,700 feet and has been found in practically all the seas of the earth. The best clue to its character is that, for a while, it was believed to disappear at night. Later, it was discovered that towards nightfall, it begins to move towards the surface and during the night its echo mark cannot be distinguished from the surface trace on the depth recorder. This daily movement of several hundred feet suggests that the scattering layer is made up of large numbers of living creatures which are able to move vertically in the water at a rate of five to ten feet in a minute. Various theories as to the kind of creature involved have been put forward at Woods Hole, La Jolla and other oceanographic laboratories. Scientists of the Miami Marine Laboratory working with Hilary Moore have studied these movements with nets and underwater cameras and sound devices and have suggested that, from the nature of the echo and of its movements, the scattering layer may consist of the small shrimplike euphausiids which make up the animal plankton in many parts of the open ocean. Unfortunately, it is difficult to identify the scattering layer with certainty, since nets fine enough to catch this kind of plankton have not, so far, caught the "scatterers" in large enough number to be absolutely sure.

Whatever the scattering layer consists of, it is undoubtedly some kind of living planktonic organism and it points to a considerable concentration of life at this depth, a concentration that could well support fast-moving midwater fishes

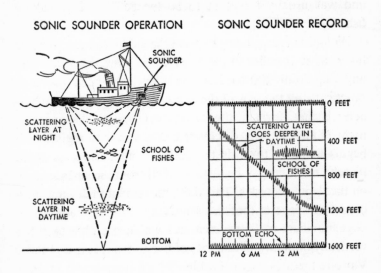

*Figure 12.* Use of the sonic sounder for recording both the depth of water and the presence of schools of fish—or of a scattering layer.

that may not school in sufficient density to appear themselves on the echo trace. Whatever this layer is we can be pretty sure it is a possible source of food in one form or another, perhaps even of small fishes themselves.

In this brief account of new methods and the need to develop more fully the mechanics of commercial fishing and fish-locating it is easy to see that man is now ready to assail a new frontier of supply. Planes hovering above the waves and electronic devices penetrating forward and around the waters where the fishing vessels cruise are beginning to take the blind gamble out of fishing for profit just as they have already helped the whaling industry. And beyond this, the fact that television cameras can be lowered into heretofore unexplored areas of the deep and that Piccard has touched the two mile bottom of the Tyrrhenian Sea in his latest diving craft, indicate that the unknown factors of the sea's mystery must soon give way to scientific inspection. But this is not the hitch. The economy of bringing the riches of the sea to our table at reasonable price, the sacred price structure of the business of fishing, is where the pattern of more protein from the sea breaks down. Fish are perishable, are found often far from their natural market and require a high capital outlay in modern equipment.

It is true that the use of factory ships is increasing whereby much of the preservation and processing is done at the source when the fish are hauled aboard fresh from the deep. The United States government has forwarded experimental work in factory ships, particulary in the Pacific, with varying success. In the salmon fisheries it has been found that freezing aboard ship has paid off and this is being extended to the king-crab and bottom fisheries near Alaska. But vessels catching shrimp in the Gulf of Mexico have found that freezing at sea has not so far been profitable. One vessel, the 8,800 ton *Pacific Explorer*, equipped as an experimental vessel for filleting, freezing, canning, salting and by-product reduction operations, has operated in the Bering Sea in summer and more southerly waters the rest of the year. Much useful information has been gathered from these trials, and this type of vessel may well lead to operations at a profit in the rich fishing waters off the western coast of South America. The freezing of whole fish at sea helps cut labor costs, permits a longer stay on the grounds and opens up the prospect of putting trash fish, heretofore wasted, to useful purpose as fertilizers. But this has been done with government subsidy. Until the demand from the consumer warrants further expansion, it is unlikely that sufficient capital will be forthcoming from private sources. The consensus of the experts at United Nations Conference in 1949 was that research must go along with a concerted and subsidized effort to attack the fisheries problem from the economic point of view before our world, in face of great population increases, can be supplied with a greatly augmented supply of a cheap and abundant source of high protein food from the sea to those who are in need of it.

The sea is potentially more valuable as an area of increased future food resource than the land and yet in proportion the amount of study devoted to the sea acreage is negligible compared to that given to our overworked land resources. Augmented study is greatly needed but it should not be one sided. It must develop, not only the engineering for finding, catching, processing and marketing, but also the basic oceanography of the sea. Only thus will our knowledge of the total environment of the undersea open up new frontiers of exploitation.

We have so far considered the efforts being made to develop our marine food resources by the application of engineering, technology and basic oceanographic research to the hunting of fishes. Before we turn to the mineral and energy resources of the sea we must also consider to what extent science and technology have helped us to harvest the vegetation and fishes of the sea by farming, by the controlled captive exploitation of the sea plants and sea fishes.

# CHAPTER 5

# Farming for Fishes

BECAUSE OF THE UNTAMED AND ELE-
mental nature of the sea it is the last area of the globe that
man has to conquer and bend to the uses of his civilization.
Conquer is a poor word to use, perhaps, because it means
ravage, rape and exploit as well as intelligently dominate.
The oceans have been fairly impervious to the good or ill
man can administer in his ardent "conquest" of nature.
Today, we approach the sea as men three hundred years
ago attacked the virgin continent of America. We hunt, trap
and begin to cultivate the margins of a half known area of
vast resource. It is easy for a landsman to pose the question
of why we do not apply the same energy of scientific engineering to the sea that we have learned so well to do in
our agricultural advance on land. But the sea is really another world where the potential harvests are alive, on the
move both vertically and horizontally, and where the
farmers of the sea cannot readily build on and fence in such
acreage as the Grand Banks.

Wherever the land is right for it, we can have our herds
of beasts and control our pasturage and calculate the result-
ing food per acre. We can further improve our output by

selective breeding of the creatures themselves and the provender they consume. Can this be done with the ocean herbivores, the fishes which are the flesh of the sea? Attempts have been made for a long time to do this on the fringes of the sea in many countries. At first sight it is natural to conclude that such attempts must be too trivial to count because of the extent and depth of the oceans and the untrammelled alien nature of the waters. Nevertheless, such attempts have been made with some success and benefit to mankind.

In general, three methods have been mainly followed in our effort to farm the ocean waters. In point of time the oldest practice, dating back many centuries, has been the cultivation of fishes in ponds and inlets of the sea, closed off and captive. Then, in comparatively recent times, during the nineteenth century artificial fertilization of eggs was tried successfully and the small fry or larvae were held in hatcheries until considered old enough to release into ocean waters with the hope that this would increase depleted natural stocks. In other places, the practice of transplanting young adult fishes from areas of abundance to areas in which the fish in question had never lived was tried in an endeavor to build completely fresh stocks. In addition to this method, transplantations have been made from overcrowded environments to less crowded areas where plentiful food allowed a more rapid growth. Man is only beginning to probe the potential of such methods of development and it is well worth asking just how far we can push these practices beyond what we are doing today.

Past studies in marine biology have emphasized the enormous reproductive possibilities possessed by most fishes and have created an intense interest in their cultivation and in the development of hatcheries and new methods of transplanting and restocking the supply of edible fishes in the sea. In the nineteenth century, biologists argued that natural propagation was inefficient and that man, by supplementing nature through the artificial fertilization of eggs by newly discovered methods, offered a far more efficient way of increasing natural populations than nature itself could accomplish unaided. The enthusiasm for this view is well illustrated by Bower, who wrote in 1898: "due proportion must be taken from their spawning grounds so that sufficient ova may be touched by the magic wand of protected propagation to provide for future crops."

About a hundred years ago fish culturists discovered that they could artificially fertilize fishes by stripping the milt and eggs from males and females and mixing them together under controlled conditions. By exercising reasonable precautions against changes of temperature, lack of aeration and mechanical shock, it was found that fertilized eggs and young fishes could be carefully transported over considerable distances. This set in motion a great wave of poorly planned hatching and transplantation where enthusiasm overbalanced careful scientific observation; for in most cases no adequate analysis was made of end results and it was often found, when checks were made, that there were no detectable benefits whatsoever.

But in spite of many failures several extremely successful transplantations came off, notably the transfer of shad from the east to the west coast waters of the United States. The shad is a salt-water fish of the herring family which swims up the coastal rivers in the springtime to spawn. The first attempt at releasing artificially fertilized larvae of shad was made in 1848 in the waters of rivers entering the Gulf of Mexico, but it met with failure. Likewise, between 1873 and 1892 large numbers of these baby shad were hopefully placed in the Colorado River and even in the very saline waters of the Great Salt Lake. In these cases also the fish failed to develop or to reproduce in their new environment. But about this same time over 600,000 larvae were taken from the Hudson River and turned loose in the Sacramento River and another million released in areas north of San Francisco Bay. Here, at long last, a favorable new environment was discovered and the young shad developed so well in succeeding generations that they have spread from Southern California to Alaska. This success can be measured in terms of food for man by the fact that the take of 100,000 pounds in 1888 has risen to a catch of 4,000,000 pounds of shad today. Here, indeed, is an example of what can be done when fishes are transplanted to areas lacking such species and where the environment is perfectly suited to their specific needs.

Another Atlantic food fish transferred cross-continent to a strange ocean with signal success is the striped bass. This fish has somewhat similar habits to the shad and was completely foreign to Californian waters although abundant in the East all the way from Florida to the Gulf of St. Lawrence. This transfer was a natural follow-up of the good results with shad and in 1879 to 1882 less than 500 fish between one and ten inches long were taken from New Jersey to the Pacific coast. So apt were the striped bass to these new waters that by the end of the century the descendants of the pioneer five hundred were supplying commercial fisheries with over a million pounds a year, which doubled by 1904. Today this is one of the most important game fishes of California.

This experiment, so obviously successful in itself, brings up an important problem arising from the success in transplanting a single species of fishes, namely, that there is a possibility that the striped bass may have a detrimental effect on the native Pacific salmon population. Admirable though an invasion may be in some aspects, it may still be hard on the old inhabitants. There is, of course, nothing to be gained by introducing a new species in an environment if it upsets the natural balance in competition for food or for other reasons, so that the newcomers merely replace a similar number of a more valuable native fish.

In spite of the record of success in the two transplantations just mentioned, there are few records of other such attempts succeeding, which is a good enough indication of the many complicated factors involved beyond the mere physical introduction of healthy fish into a new environment. Much closer coordinated study of saltiness and temperature, food and the natural enemies of fishes must yet be made before the practices followed with good luck in the case of shad and bass can be intelligently applied on a larger and more scientific scale. One other case, however, should be noted, namely, the transference of trout and salmon from Great Britain to New Zealand where they now live in great abundance in the rivers. But we cannot consider this a completely successful case of sea transplantation because in New Zealand the salmon remains in fresh waters and no longer takes to the sea. Why they do not duplicate their long European migration to mid-Atlantic by a similar migration into the Pacific waters is hard to explain and seems to be one of the unsolved mysteries of the instinctive actions that so much control the life of fishes in general.

Transplantation by man is used in another fashion than that of seeking a totally new environment for a species. This is when fishes are taken in quantity from an unsuitable or overcrowded neighborhood and placed in one that is less crowded—a sort of slum clearance, in fact, aimed at better living conditions. This interesting work has been carried out successfully on a large scale in European waters with plaice by the Danes. The plaice is a bottom-living flat fish which lays its eggs during the winter in the warmer waters of the North Sea. As these eggs develop into young fish they drift towards the coasts of Holland and Denmark. From the Danish seacoast a narrow channel connects the North Sea with an extensive system of sheltered waters called the Limfjord. In the western neck of this semi-enclosed system of waters there are large numbers of plaice but they remain small in size. They have migrated here from the open North Sea but because of overcrowding there is too much competition for food and they do not develop well. Some few of these Limfjord plaice penetrate, however, through the inland waters and reach broad inner eastern reaches of the fjord and these few grow more rapidly and to greater size. But the fish do not breed in this better inside environment. So, a trial was attempted to make use of the superior feeding grounds by transplanting small plaice from the overcrowded western end of the fjord to the eastern end where they could find more room and better food. The first experiment was made in 1892 with some 80,000 fish. Many of them were tagged for observation and when recaught it was found that these fish, less than ten inches in length originally and weighing less than a quarter of a pound, had increased as much as five times their weight during a period of six months after transplantation. Since 1908 between one and three million plaice have been transplanted each year, except when the project was interrupted by war. This scheme, technically so successful, has also been commercially a boon to the Danes as the value of the increased catch has been more than five times the cost of the effort.

The North Sea, which has been heavily fished for centuries by the Scandinavian countries, England, and Holland, may truly be said to be one of the few seas that have been overfished. The most striking area where this has occurred is in the Belt Sea plaice fisheries surrounding the Danish islands of Seeland and Fiinen. But here again man stepped in to remedy shortages he himself had created, by bringing to the Belt from one to two million plaice each year from Horn's Reef, an overcrowded area of undersized fish. This experiment has been most successful, except of course for the interruption of World War II. It is interesting to note that the plaice transferred from the North Sea to the Belt are of a slightly different race and when liberated in the Belt Sea grow at a much greater rate than the local race of fish.

Other transplantations similar to the Danish experiments but on a small scale have been made in European waters. This shows that man can do much to augment his food supply from the sea when he is aware of the natural conditions at hand and aims to cooperate with nature rather than to make a blind stab at a bonanza result which may fail or even adversely affect the delicate biological balance. It has been demonstrated, for instance, that it is economically sound to transplant young plaice from the over-populated English and Danish inshore areas to the Dogger Bank, in the North Sea, to which the young plaice are prevented from migrating by the intervention of deep waters. On the Dogger Bank they grow about four times as rapidly as they do in their original location. Calculations have shown that there are, crowded in the Horn's Reef area, well over 100 million young, undersized plaice at the age and growth appropriate to transplantation. Moving a large proportion of these would benefit rather than harm the fishing in that locality.

Actual experience makes it clear, then, that transplantation under favorable conditions can be both biologically and economically successful in establishing a new fishery or in bringing about a healthy increase in production in a fishery long established. It has also been well demonstrated by experience, and by the large numbers of unsuccessful transplantations due to unfavorable environment and the competition set up between new stocks and endemic or native stocks, that there are sufficient reasons to go slow. So, if man is going to join the dance, he had better know the steps; in other words, before rushing hopefully into new projects, careful scientific study is imperative.

Scientists being human are not immune to enthusiasms and fads, and scientific opinion tends to move in cycles, first pushing one theory and then another. The realization in mid-nineteenth century that our fisheries were not inexhaustible or limitless led to overstress of the role of fish hatcheries as an answer and brought them into fashion. There was a great wave of attempts to restock the sea fisheries with larvae and small fry artificially hatched by man. In the

United States, Great Britain and Norway, in particular, the hatching of marine food fishes was carried out on a large scale but with results that are now considered to be of questionable value, if not demonstrably worthless.

Take as an example the large shad hatcheries of the United States which have released as many as 400 million fry in a single year and yet have failed to prevent a decline of the fishery. Little has been done to study the effects of this kind of restocking in any detail except in Europe. One of the few careful measures of the effectiveness of hatching was made in Scotland at the beginning of the century. More than 142 million young plaice were released from hatcheries into Loch Fyne each year. Then the yearly effect of this addition upon the numbers of commercial-size plaice in the loch was measured by comparing the catch of years when fry were added, with the catch of years when they were not added. The result showed, naturally enough, an increase in the young fry because of their release but bore little relation to the size of the commercial catch, as some of the heaviest releases of fry coincided with a poor catch of grown fish. It is therefore apparent that the large fluctuations which naturally occur in sea fish stocks are substantially greater than the effects of hatchery operations. Only in a year when an additional 50 million fry were released in Loch Fyne, equivalent to 10 percent of the eggs naturally produced, did the fry release make a really appreciable difference to the catch. Similar experiments in Norway have tended to confirm the results at Loch Fyne. For instance, in 1904 when 33 million cod fry were released in one fjord the young cod were found there in unusual abundance the following autumn. But, unfortunately, so were they found in abundance in other fjords where no fry had been released. Due to another natural fluctuation of supply in 1905 all the fjords were low in codfish whether they had received artificial help from the hatcheries or not.

This does not rule out the hatcheries as aids to nature. More recent experiments tend to show that under special conditions the hatchery technique of stimulating production may be used to increase the natural yield of the fisheries or, at least, to counteract disastrous effects of natural fluctuations upon the fishing industry in bad years. Whether the costs of maintaining this type of fish farming can be economically justified is another matter. In Norway an ingenious technique was used by Rollefson for accurately checking results. He used easily recognized hybrids or cross breed plaice in his hatchery experiments, a sort of built-in biological tagging device. After release, these fish could quite readily be distinguished from the fish naturally reproduced, when sample catches were made. The tally was somewhat similar to the Loch Fyne experiments and showed that the release of fry does increase the subsequent catch of young fish but not enough to counteract the effects of naturally caused fluctuations which were even greater.

From this brief résumé of some of the trial and error experimentation done so far, it is evident that we are still only in the early stages of using fish culture or transplantation as a practical way of increasing the supply of available protein from our open sea fisheries. There is no question but that considerably more knowledge is needed regarding the causes of natural fluctuations in native fish stocks before hatchery techniques can be satisfactorily used. It is clear that merely to add newly hatched fry is rarely likely to be of value and

## TABLE I

| YEAR | NUMBER OF HYBRIDS RELEASED (*in millions*) | PERCENTAGE IN THE CATCH | RATIO |
|------|------|------|------|
| 1935 | 2 | 1.5 | 0.75 |
| 1939 | 7 | 40.0 | 5.79 |
| 1937 | 7 | 0.5 | 0.07 |
| 1938 | 10 | 96.0 | 9.6 |
| 1936 | 13 | 30.0 | 2.3 |

that even the release of partially mature fish may never be very useful except in restricted locations such as the Scottish or Norwegian lochs and fjords. Millions of fry coming from the hatcheries seem like a great quantity until we compare them to the natural productivity of the fishes involved. A single female cod, for instance, produces from one to five million eggs a year. A hatchery rarely produces more than 200 million fry a year, which after all is about the equivalent of a few female cod at work on their own without benefit of man and an expensive overhead. The lesson is simply this, that man can step into the natural cycle of production and increase results to a useful level only when he has the data and the experience to augment intelligently long-established natural processes. Man's best luck has come, as with the shad, where he has been fortunate enough to find a virgin area with an optimum environment for a transplanted species to flourish.

And this leads to a point that may someday bring further good results, namely the artificial removal by man of predatory or less valuable fish from an area, thus releasing food supply in the sea for the expansion of useful species or for the introduction of a new species in the vacancy in the food chain thus created. As a plausible instance, we might cite the benefit to shrimp of a possible removal of red-snapper from Gulf of Mexico waters since the red-snapper takes ten times its own weight in shrimp as food. Here shrimp is the more valuable sea food and has the further advantage of being a direct feeder on plankton, which is at the base of the sea's natural food scale. The same conjecture would hold if menhaden, which are not edible, although they also are direct plankton feeders, could be replaced by herring which are plankton feeders but are one of man's most useful food fish and likewise, in surplus, could also supply oil and fish meal. At present, of course, we have no practical way of interfering with the food chain except by the purposeful overfishing of the less desirable types, but this does not preclude the future development of such techniques.

The proponents of sea hatcheries admit that the success of their releases of fry depends upon natural conditions in the sea after release. But conditions thus favorable to hatchery fry are also favorable to naturally produced fish. What is really needed is a method of artificially providing more fish under unfavorable conditions. Only a small part of the eggs released in nature ever attain full growth into adult fish and it is therefore essential that the hatcheries rear their young fish beyond the stage at which the greatest mortality occurs in nature. As yet, the biological and hydrographic conditions which prevent the majority of eggs becoming adults are not too well understood, but it appears that the greatest loss in nature occurs just after the young fry has consumed all its egg yolk and is beginning to forage for

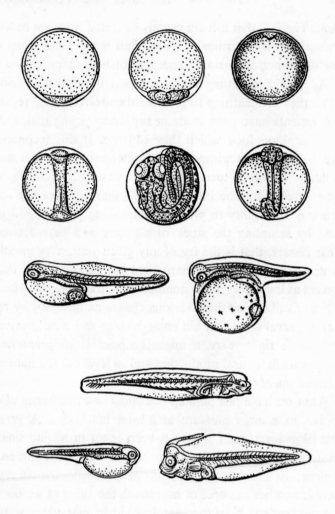

*Figure 13.* Eggs and newly hatched young of various sea fishes.

itself. The fact that fish are usually liberated from sea hatcheries at this most critical stage of their lives is undoubtedly one of the present serious barriers to their usefulness.

As an aid to getting the larvae past the difficult period when they are learning to feed for themselves, some recent experiments have been made in supplying young plaice fry with plankton food which they can use. If this technique can be developed without greatly increasing the cost and difficulty of fish culture, then a great new era of usefulness may develop for the hatcheries. Another encouraging advance is the ability to predict poor fishing years ahead of time by sampling the stock of all ages and year classes. Year classes, that is the fry of any given year, vary greatly in numbers, due to their hard fight for survival, and thus can act as indicators of the numbers of marketable fish which will be available as these various classes mature. So, by releasing larval fish at an old enough stage to insure survival and in the right years, it might be possible to counteract poor years in natural production and to level out the natural fluctuations of numbers.

What we have just pointed out about fish hatcheries also applies in a large measure to lobster hatcheries. A great deal of government money has been spent in raising small lobsters and then releasing them into the ocean without any evidence to show that this in any way benefits the fishery. Here is another example of how much the value of artificial propagation has been over-emphasized in past years while at the same time the efficiency of natural reproduction has been underestimated. In a like degree, the freshwater hatcheries, which were the original starting point for this fashion, are still biologically unsound operations. Their actual value to conservation is nil. The planting of fingerling trout in streams is a waste of public funds since the return to the angler does not even reach 1 per cent. It has been shown, for instance, that in Michigan streams more young are naturally produced than the waters and available food can support.

On the other hand, the rearing of fish to a legal size old enough to briefly fend for themselves, is a most expensive operation. Far from being good fishery management or conservation, it is no more justified biologically than if the anglers were to catch them directly from the hatchery ponds. It remains, however, the only means of satisfying many amateur pioneers with rods and a license, and a vote. In the case of the sea fisheries, it would be even more expensive to raise adult fishes or lobsters and certainly foolish to release them into the open sea rather than directly into market baskets.

A problem still to be considered which may need the application of the best hatchery techniques merely to survive, is that of our extensive salmon fisheries. The salmon is not only an ocean fish caught at the entrance to rivers as well as at sea but is one that has to seek the upper reaches of fresh water streams to breed. Therefore, man added extra hazards to its existence when he brought in dams, hydroelectric projects and the chemical pollution of the streams by factories. The heavy exploitation of the salmon fisheries has already commenced its decline. Successful salmon hatchery operation, as well as more extended construction of fish ladders and by-passes for spawning salmon ascending the rivers, is badly needed to counteract man's interference with the natural cycle of the salmon's life.

So it is not hard to see that whatever we have done in artificial propagation or transplanting of young fish falls far short of the full control needed or of the control that a farmer has, for instance, over his fields and his cattle. The released fry or transplanted fish have for the most part to be let loose without restraint so that their capture and use by man depends once more on the old hunting techniques. But there is a closer approach to our land control of food animals in the practice of pond culture of fishes in which they are restricted to comparatively small bodies of water and are fed and cared for to the point where they are as domesticated as cattle.

The greater portion of fish-pond culture is carried out in fresh-water lakes or ponds. But the pond culture of salt-water or brackish-water fishes is widespread among the less industrialized people of the Far East, in the Philippines, Indonesia, India and China. This art has been developed for at least 500 years in Java, where today over 15 per cent of all the protein in the diet comes from fish ponds. It is legendary in Hawaii that there were extensive pond-culture fisheries at Pearl Harbor three hundred years ago. In spite of this antiquity and the undoubted value of pond fisheries as a supply of food, only in recent years has Western man begun to make any serious study of it. In the East today the fish-pond culture is carried on for the most part by old-time rule-of-thumb methods without regard to scientific knowledge.

In Batavia, Singapore and Formosa most of the salt-water ponds are simply fish-traps with gates which allow the fish to enter at high tide. Once caught they are held to grow and fatten in the ponds. The great disadvantage of this method, of course, is the lack of selection which permits the enemies and predators of useful food fishes to be trapped along with them and so keeps the final yield unnecessarily low. In recent years an advance in this practice has been made by catching the young fry from the sea and releasing them in specially prepared ponds free of hostile fishes.

Where the deep-sea fishing has not been developed and the pressure of a poor and hungry population has long existed, such as in the Philippines and Indonesia, great use has been made of the pond culture of the bañgo or milkfish. In the Philippine Islands alone, an industry involving a capital outlay of 150 million dollars provides about 17 million pounds of fish annually. This is particularly true for the Manila area where the bañgo is the principal protein food. After hundreds of years of slow development, pond culture here has reached the stage where it precludes predatory fishes and goes beyond that to ensure the correct type of food for the milkfish at various stages of its growth. No fertilizer is added to these ponds but there is probably a good deal of natural drainage which helps to feed the native aquatic vegetable growth. Every few years most ponds are drained and the bottom silt is plowed and turned over, thus stirring up sediments which probably add to their fertility. Philippine milkfish spawn offshore from the sandy coasts and then the young fry move inshore where they can be readily captured. They are first put into ponds where a bottom growth of blue-green algae provides a natural food. After they are about three inches long the young fish are transferred to ponds with a different growth of green filamentous seaweed appropriate to this stage. Sometimes the fish are transferred again before finally reaching marketable age. The care of the fish during the different stages of growth is frequently handled by men skilled as specialists in the different phases of pond culture.

Once again pond culture illustrates the advantage of the immediate transfer of vegetable food into protein without the intermediate steps from grazing fish, to small carnivorous fish, to larger and larger fish until suitable for commercial use. There is a minimum loss of energy in the process of conversion from one stage of the food chain to another instead of an increasing loss through several successive conversions. Let's look at it this way. One thousand tons of vegetable plankton converted by grazing to animal plankton, then to plankton-feeding fishes and finally to carnivorous fishes will in the end only supply one ton of fish; then compare the fact that this same 1,000 tons of vegetable algae in the salt ponds, when converted directly as food to the milkfish, will yield about 100 tons of fish. Here by short-cutting the chain of conversion, man arrives at a hundred times better production of protein food.

Many thousands of miles of low-lying coastal swamp country in the tropics and subtropics, not at present under pond culture, would make favorable areas for an extension of fish farming from a purely biological point of view. In many ways the yield of food is better than that of direct agricultural land production. In China, for instance, pond culture is said to yield as much as 5,000 to 7,000 pounds of fish flesh per acre, compared to 800 pounds per acre for beef on the best grazing lands.

But there are good reasons why a greater use of this form of food production has not greatly increased in many years.

In the first place, science has only made a beginning in the study of pond cultures. These have survived on a trial-and-error, empirical basis depending on local necessity, namely, dense human populations with a low standard of living. This creates the cheap labor required in pond upkeep and also no doubt furnishes, through natural drainage, a considerable supply of human fertilizer. All the factors—economic, social and particularly biological—need joint study before the potentially suitable areas around the seacoasts of the world can successfully be added to present production. There is no use having a good source of food so far removed from a concentrated market that it is economically impossible to use it. And further, in spite of a possible great increase in pond culture, this type of production still would only be a relatively small fraction of the full ocean food potential.

Before leaving this subject of fish-farms we should look at the story of oyster cultivation which is one of man's most successful attempts to control salt-water food supply. This culture, like that of fish ponds, is of ancient origin. Two thousand years ago the Romans at Brundusium collected oysters and transplanted them to the Lucrine area to protect them from storms, and even erected buildings along the shore to break the force of the winds. The growing oysters were attached to ropes which hung in the water between stakes while they were fattening. This has a parallel modern practice and, as a matter of fact, Dr. Costé of France, who saved the French oyster industry almost singlehanded by his investigations in the late nineteenth century, started his studies with the traditional Italian methods.

Today, oysters are cultivated all over the world where

conditions are favorable, in Australia, Japan, the United States, France, England, Holland and as far north as Norway. The methods differ in detail but on the whole are necessarily dictated by the peculiarities of the oyster's way of life. These are interesting because they well illustrate the conditions of prolific breeding and tremendous destruction of young life that is common to the cycle of growth of many sea creatures. Because oysters grow in shallow waters, man has been able to study their life cycle in great detail. They live out their adult life in fixed positions and are susceptible to easy handling and transplanting by man.

Essentially the oyster is a pump, a sort of submarine vacuum cleaner and a single small shellfish can pass as much as a hundred gallons of water a day through its system sorting out the minute plankton and algae it needs for food and rejecting the debris. It is evident that the type and purity of the water the oysters live in is of the utmost importance. So likewise is the salinity and temperature of the water. Oysters must have an admixture of fresh water with the salt and they therefore thrive in estuaries. This reduced salinity tends to protect them as well from the drills and starfish which are among their greatest enemies. Though quiet, conservative and fixed in his habits when grown, the young oyster has an adventurous, rough life. It survives not necessarily because it is the fittest but by the pure hazard of where it finds itself at the end of a helpless initial period of drifting in the waters. We must fumble in describing the sex of the oyster as it is a strange creature which usually starts as a male in the first breeding season and then alternates male and female thereafter. The fertilized eggs drift as part of the plankton for two to three weeks. One oyster produces several million

young of which only a comparatively few ever survive to
maturity. From a purely statistical point of view, if this
prodigious mortality did not occur, the progeny of only two
or three dozen oysters would within a short time be sufficient to feed the entire world population.

From the plankton stage the small spat settle to the bottom and unless they find a clean bottom where they can
attach themselves to rock or sand they perish from silt, overcrowding, pollution and other natural enemies to their development. This is the most critical phase of their existence
and the point where man by artificial means can best pro-
mote their growth. At that, a scant few find this suitable
bottom and not many among this residue ever live to maturity. About the only self-preserving instinct an oyster has
is a tendency for the young spat to seek, to some extent, their
own kind. They flourish better in colonies.

Dr. Costé first introduced modern practices of conservation in Western oyster culture at Arcachon in France. Here
in a great shallow bay the oyster larvae are collected in
enormous quantities on curved roofing tiles which have first
been coated with lime and sand. After the spat attached to
the tiles have been allowed sufficient time to make their pre-
liminary growth, they are broken off by simply flaking away
the lime coating and are then placed in special trays covered
with wire netting and supported above the bottom on legs.
The young oyster is thus protected from silt, parasites and
overcrowding. Later on, as the oysters grow, they are placed
in special fattening beds. In France, at Marennes and elsewhere, there are ponds known as "claires" where the oysters
are fattened. These enclosed bodies of water are open to the
sea only at the time of the spring tides. In the summer they

warm up, become salty, and produce a heavy growth of plankton upon which the young oysters feed.

Before the culture at Arcachon was developed, the natural oyster beds of France were threatened with extinction due to over-fishing. The success of the artificial culture may be gauged by the fact that the land-locked Bay of Arcachon covering 37,000 acres produces 500 million oysters each year. The Japanese practice a similar type of oyster farming but there the young spat are collected on bamboo twigs which are placed in the spawning grounds and later the young oysters are transferred to trays and floated free of the silty bottom. Man has in this way made the oyster farming independent of suitable types of bottom.

Oyster culture in the United States has not developed the careful techniques used in Europe and in Japan. Here the old hunting culture persists and many of the oysters are produced in public waters where the methods of dredging, rather than the culture, are paramount. The need for developing cultivation practices in oyster farming in the United States is well illustrated by the fact that even though the majority of oyster beds are on public bottoms, nevertheless, over 60 per cent of the production comes from the smaller, privately cultivated areas. A vastly greater production could be brought about if good practices of cultivation were more general. Indeed, with the large mechanical dredgers and harvesters now in use in the United States, an expanded and more elaborate system of cultivation could probably give us three times the present yield. Let us take Holland as an example. Between the years 1840 and 1870 the public bottoms raised anywhere from half a million to two million oysters each year and these were poor in size or shape. After that country established a supervised and intensive cultivation of these same areas, the production was raised to 30 or 40 million oysters a year—and of superior quality.

The reason for going into some detail on oyster culture is the obvious fact that, along with fish farming in ponds, it illustrates one of the best ways of increasing and utilizing the tremendous initial productivity of the sea. Oysters, because they feed on plant life and the vegetable detritus of shallow waters, are at the very bottom of the food chain of the sea and can therefore use the ocean productivity almost at full. This holds true for other molluscs such as the mussel which is reported to produce as much as 6,000 pounds to the acre where cultivated in Holland. This may be compared to the highest production of free-swimming fish which, at the best, in such places as the Sea of Azov yields only 40 to 70 pounds per acre per year. It is plain that man will obtain protein from the sea with least waste of energy when he is able to harvest it at the lower end of the food chain.

As we survey the past efforts of man to enhance the natural end-product of nature in the seas—that is, the supply of protein for his table—the original thesis of the necessity of changing the rather blind instinctive hunting economy into the controlled practices and techniques of a sea-farming economy is evident. It is also evident that increasing our engineering skills is not enough unless the basic biological understanding is likewise developed. Practices used in pond culture and oyster culture, where man abets nature in producing from the primary end of the food chain with the least loss of energy, certainly encourage optimism though there are limitations of space.

Today, with modern methods of transport such as the airplane, and modern methods of cooling and refrigeration, the transplantation of fry and even larger fish has been greatly improved. But we have learned from earlier haphazard experimentation that it does no good to glut overpopulated areas or hopefully to populate areas barren of food or where other factors of environment, such as temperature or salinity, are unfavorable. Further, we must avoid situations where transplanted fishes will only multiply at the expense of more valuable native species or even where they may bring with them damaging parasites or new diseases. In a word, man cannot upset established biological balance in an area without risking unforeseen and dangerous consequences. The naive transplanting of rabbits to Australia is a case in point. All this points to the need of greatly increased biological and hydrographic studies. At the present moment such studies are urgently called for, both in the salmon industry of the Pacific coast, and to further our sparse knowledge of unexploited coastal waters in the tropics and the Southern Hemisphere.

Although once man thought he could automatically increase the fish populations by the mere transplanting of fry, at the present moment it is difficult to estimate what new sources transplantation may open in the future. It is reasonable to expect that this method, though it has had occasional spectacular results, will not make too great a change relative to our total production from the salt ocean. Limited transplantations from nursery grounds to fattening grounds, as in the case of the North Sea plaice, have been undoubtedly valuable, but such transplantations are more or less limited to shallow coastal areas and will only serve to make an insignificant increase in relation to the total world production.

Hatching will have greater value as we are better able to raise the young fry beyond the critical stage at which they lose their egg sacks and begin to forage for themselves. But even here, successful practice will probably be restricted to semi-enclosed and protected waters such as fjords and lochs.

The importance of salt-water fish ponds and the supervised culture of oysters and shellfish lies in the fact that they are primary consumers of plankton and algae. But here again, as we have shown, the areas susceptible to such development are limited both geographically by the nature of coastal waters and by the ready availability of labor and a market. The continental shelves are most extensive in the Northern Hemisphere and constitute only 7½ percent of our seas and oceans. The fringing coastal areas, sufficiently shallow and otherwise suitable for pond culture and shellfishes, are again only a small proportion of these continental shelves. Even so, with our present knowledge of oyster, mussel and clam production, it is probable we could at least treble the 4 percent of our total fish consumption which they now represent.

It is obvious from this review of the situation that this type of study, and subsequent beneficial increase in protein from fish life in the sea, is attacked with a great initial advantage at the beginning of the food chain which starts with the vegetable and animal plankton that appears everywhere in the vast pastures of the ocean. It is reasonable, then, to look to the cultivation and the farming of sea plants, seaweeds and the plankton as the most efficient way of extracting a maximum yield of food from salt water. This is an inquiry in itself and will, therefore, follow as the principal subject of discussion in our next chapter.

# CHAPTER 6

## *Ocean Pasturage*

ON LAND IT IS ROUGHLY TRUE THAT nine-tenths of the green food eaten by animals serves merely to sustain life, so that one-tenth alone is left to sustain permanent growth. And so it takes many more acres to grow a ton of beef than it does to grow a ton of hay or of sugar beets. For this reason we may well consider a return to vegetarian diet as one way of multiplying our food supply many times. What is true of the land applies just as well to the sea. The advantages we gain by harvesting land vegetables rather than beef are small in comparison to those we might gain were we to harvest plankton instead of fishes. By reason of the longer chain of creatures and fishes which intervene between man and the plankton, we may enormously increase the yield of food from the ocean by going directly to the plants—by as much as a thousand or more times. So plankton may be seen as the base of a great food pyramid, with man, the ultimate recipient of a small, much diminished bounty, at its apex.

Plankton is not the only sea pasturage, not alone in being a direct recipient of solar energy in the sea. Together with

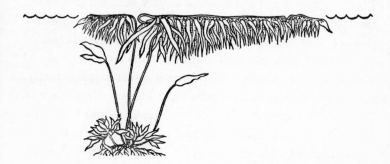

*Figure 14.* The big kelp of California, *Macrocystis pyrifera* may grow up to a length of 150 feet so that it can grow in 20 fathoms of water. The leafy part floats on the surface and hence is easily mown off. This is a source of alginic acid.

the tiny drifting cells there is also a sea growth which is in some ways more readily available to man, and this consists of the varied kinds of seaweeds which crowd our shorelines. Since they are the closest to hand we shall first consider what use man has made and could make of them in harvesting the vegetation of the ocean. Few of us have ever seen plankton but most are familiar with the seaweeds along the shallow fringes of the coastline. They are limited to such waters simply because they are anchored to the sea bottom and their leaves must reach the surface waters for light. For many years man has harvested them for food, fertilizer, medicine or mineral. In both Europe and Japan sea-wrack, kelp or tangle, by whatever local name it was known, has been used in fresh or half-rotted condition for fertilizer and, burnt down to ash, has been a source of iodine, soda and potash. But aside from a simple and handy source of fertilizer its other uses have become largely obsolete due to the modern discovery of mineral deposits more economically worked. But modern chemistry has also discovered special commercial uses for such algal products as agar and the alginic acids and even if these are a rather small industry, seaweed still remains as a possible source of chemicals and minerals if and when engineering, chemical, and biological techniques can efficiently combine to give it a useful market. All these sciences must be brought into team play before we can make full use of our ocean resources in general and the history of seaweed utilization affords a very clear example of this need.

Plants useful to man on land that give us wood, fiber, fruit and root crops are all members of the so-called flowering vegetation and rank high in the scale of evolution. The few specialized flowering plants of this kind in the sea are of little importance. The seaweeds are quite different. They are algae, plants which reproduce by spores and are low in the evolutionary scale. Their patterns, caught in ancient rock formations, date them among the earliest forms of life on earth. These sea algae are easily distinguished by their color; green, blue-green, brown and red. The brown and the red types are the only ones of any economic importance and the brown seaweeds are the most widespread in the temperate zones of both hemispheres along rocky sea coasts. They are found most abundantly between the tide marks to about 60 feet below the tidal line. The smallest of these, like the Irish Moss, are only a few inches in length while the larger kelp of the Pacific coast range up to more than a hundred feet in length. Very often they are provided with air or gas bladders that keep the leaves afloat in the surface waters reaching for sunlight while their roots are attached to the bottom by long tough rubbery stalks.

These brown seaweeds are valuable to us because they form a natural chemical factory which extracts minerals from the sea and concentrates them in the leaves to a greater degree than they exist in the water itself. Also, just as land plants do, seaweeds manufacture within their leaves various compounds that can be used for food, medicine and a variety of delicate industrial purposes. In Scotland, the tangle or kelp of the western coasts and the islands have long been used as a fertilizing mulch on the land just as in Ireland and France, But this is a hard practice due to the slippery bulk of the weed and has never risen above a local necessity when there has been a lack of better fertilizers. As far back as the fifteen-hundreds a Welsh writer thus describes it: "After spring tides or great rigs of the sea, they fetch it (the kelp) in sacks or horse backes, and carie the same three, four or five miles and caste it on the lands, which doth very much better the ground for corn and grass. This kind of ore they often gather and lay in heaps where it heteth and roteth and will have a strong and loathsome smell; when being so rotten they caste it on the lande as they do their muck, and therefrom springeth good corn and especially barley." Scientists today tell us that the total amount of fertilizing constituents present in fresh seaweed is comparable to the amount present in barnyard manure, although seaweed contains a much greater proportion of potassium salts, a much smaller proportion of phosphorus, and about an equal amount of nitrogen. This makes it particularly desirable for root crops, for which, of course, it has been extensively used in Ireland.

The first commercial use of the weed for minerals was in France in the seventeenth century where it was burned for soda and potash. The soda was used in making glass and pottery and at that time seaweed was the only source. Early in the nineteenth century the burnt weed was also used for the production of iodine at Cherbourg but by 1873 iodine mineral salts were discovered in Chile and the local industry died out. This is a good example of how the use of natural materials is not simply a problem of chemical know-how. The economics of stepped-up commercial competition is also a factor to be considered. For a like reason the potash industry from kelp fell on hard times with the discovery of the rock mineral deposits at Stassfurt. But even today the Japanese persist in the manufacture of iodine from seaweeds to a limited extent. In 1916 the Japanese made some 300 tons of iodine from the sea though the earlier European industry never reached more than 200 tons a year. Cheap labor accounts for the persistence of local manufacture in Japan.

During World War I when artificial strain was placed on the normal pattern of international trade, both potash and acetone were manufactured from kelp in California but by 1923 the resumption of normal peacetime competition killed this off. It is easy to realize the importance of labor costs in this kelp industry, when we find that seven thousand tons of kelp are needed to produce seven hundred tons of dry weed and from this, one ton of iodine. Similarly 80 tons of weed make one ton of potash.

Although this particular use for the weed has been superseded, new uses for kelp have been developed by modern chemistry especially for the manufacture of alginic acid.

Alginic acid and its various salts have a variety of industrial uses, especially in textiles where they are used for dressing and polishing cloth, as carriers for textile dies and in fine woolen goods where alginic fibers are woven into the wool and then dissolved out, leaving light, porous and warm material. They are also used in paper and cardboard manufacture, for emulsifying paints, as a stabilizer in ice cream, cheeses and in candy, as well as in the preparation of rubber and ink. At present the United States processes about two million pounds of alginic acid every year.

In addition to the use of brown kelp for manures and for the various industrial products, there is also some food value in it because of carbohydrates and mineral salts but there is little present promise of its being an important source of the much needed expansion of our food resources from the sea, since the carbohydrates are mostly indigestible. The use of the weed as food in Japan has been due to the pressure of population on limited supplies of more nourishing foods rather than to intrinsic value. In 1936, for instance, over 50,000 tons of finished product were used in Japan where the raw material is drawn and reduced to a gelatinous pulp, then frozen, dried and pressed and marketed as kombu or wakame in shredded form for soups and light refreshment. But the fact that brown kelp is still being harvested in Europe, Russia, Japan and along the American coasts is due to its industrial uses rather than its importance as a food for man.

The red algae or seaweeds grow throughout the world close inshore in the tidal zones. They are consumed directly as food but have particular value for the manufacture of agar which has widespread use as a base for jellies, confectionery, salad dressing, dairy products and cosmetics as well as in bacteriological techniques. About six million pounds of agar is produced annually, mostly in Japan. About 200,000 pounds of this is manufactured in the United States and small amounts in other countries throughout the world where the weed grows on the sea coasts. A gelatinous food like blanc mange is made from types of red algae in various countries. In Ireland the most common is called Irish Moss and there are also types called laver and dulse.

The Japanese make a red seaweed dish they call "nori." The basic commercial form of this product is called carrageenin and used to be made in some quantity in Massachusetts, at Scituate, but the production dropped from 750,000 pounds in 1898 to about 116,000 pounds in 1924. Already Canada uses a half a million pounds annually of such products as carrageenin. Canada has been exporting raw seaweeds at 10 cents a pound and importing finished derivatives at $1.90 a pound. Modern industrial growth demands an expansion of its home production and so the Canadian government has announced a new seaweed processing plant for Kentville, Nova Scotia, which will be subsidized for industrial research and experimentation.

It is possible, of course, that new techniques in harvesting edible seaweeds and in manufacturing a uniform product may in the future somewhat expand their use as food. But in spite of the fact that they are at the base of the food pyramid, the limited coastal areas in which they can grow is the controlling factor. They can only thrive in a very narrow marginal belt of coastal waters which form a tiny fraction of the seas, scarcely more than an average of a quarter mile along the fringe of salt waters. Nevertheless, estimates of the potential seaweed production throughout the world suggest a harvest of wet weed of about a hundred million tons per annum. This would be greatly reduced in the finished products. Although they are a potential carbohydrate source, yet, aside from exceptional wartime demand, the seaweeds contribute a negligible share of the future resources of the sea. This is due to their limited range of growth and to the cost and difficulties of harvesting and processing except where labor costs are substandard. A barge with underwater cutters has been developed in California that can harvest 500 tons of weed a day in contrast with the hand cutting from small boats still practiced in Japan. In Scotland, during World War I the government established a Seaweed Research Association which has done much to encourage and develop the industry along those shores but there is little ground at the moment for expecting much expansion of the industry in peacetime. A. W. Allen, in 1923, summarized the case thus: "Technology without economics is doomed to failure. No stable market can be expected until the products of a plant are of standard grade and quality, and until a steady supply is available with no reason to expect the discontinuance of operations."

We have first described the seaweeds because they are an accustomed crop which most of us know about and they behave in sufficiently normal patterns of growth to be readily understood; but they in no way can compare in importance with the universal plankton as a part of the extensive and rich sea pasturage. Our principal hope of greatly increasing our protein and carbohydrates from the sea lies with the more prevalent and faster-growing drift of the minute sea pasturage. The importance of plankton as an energy source is due to the enormous quantity present in the sea and its rapid turnover or cycle of growth. In an earlier chapter we briefly described it as a horde of minute sea life, both vegetable and animal, floating invisibly in the surface waters of the oceans. We spoke there of its seasons of growth and its areas of plenty or scarcity depending on sunlight, temperature, fertility and horizontal and vertical movements of currents.

Plankton has been under our nose but out of sight or sound during the long development of man on land from the purely hunting stage to the highly efficient and mechanized agricultural stage of modern society. Over a hundred years ago, in 1845, Johannes Müller for the first time poured sea water through a fine mesh net and extracted some of these minute inhabitants of the deep, heretofore neglected by man. Later, he towed the net through the sea and was amazed at the quantity of this supply. Leeuwenhoek, of Holland, first developed the general use of the microscope in the eighteenth century and thus only in comparatively recent times have we been able to closely inspect these strangely conceived creatures. Although Müller pioneered this study, it wasn't until 1872 when the *Challenger* made her great oceanographic voyage, that plankton was more carefully observed and it began to dawn on scientists that here was the source of all the food in the sea. It might almost be said that plankton has received true recognition of its value only in the twentieth century. For that reason there has been a tendency, in view of its great potential, to talk loosely about our sea pasturage in similar terms to the discovery of vast new land acreage. But as yet we are far from availing ourselves of this new wealth due to obvious difficulties of its generally dilute distribution, the ignorance of how best to harvest the crop and the general mechanical means of bringing it to the final test of placing it on our dinner tables in a palatable and inexpensive supply.

Now we can inspect more closely this new world of strangely evolved life in relation to its value as a protein food for man and beasts. Many sketchy and optimistic predictions have been made as to plankton, due to the present widespread attention drawn towards oceanography and because man is easily persuaded and astonished by novelty and numbers and confident that his know-how makes him a ready master of the natural world. Unfortunately, it is not only the layman who has gone overboard, but also some speculative and optimistic writers adrift in the alien seas of ocean science who have failed to realize the radically different problems of exploiting the sea pastures and have seen here a great new bonanza. The world of planktonic life has only come under close observation in our own time. It exists in quantity, but to harvest, prepare and economically market a palatable and useful product are technical problems still to be solved before we can use it to alleviate the mounting hunger of a protein-starved world, where populations are rapidly outbreeding the available land resources even of modern agriculture.

Let us forget for the moment the strange beauty and fantastic forms that appear under the microscope, forego romantic predictions as to the plenty-dropping hands of Oceanus and, instead, make as objective a survey as possible of the actual crop, the potential yield and the present and future means of putting plankton into factories to make fuel and chemicals and on our tables as food at a reasonable price.

The sun gives its light energy only to the surface waters of the ocean. So the plankton, dependent on the sun, can only live in depths down to around 250 feet and this depth is but 2 per cent of the average depth of the seas. Yet because of its universal distribution the production of this ocean pasture is very high. In fact, the total vegetable production of the oceans has been estimated, for the 300 million cubic miles of the sea, as about 90 per cent of the total vegetable production of the globe. This estimate, possibly too high, has enchanted various authors, and plankton has been spoken of by Jacob Rosin and Max Eastman as "another inexhaustible source of protein." True, it is there and we know its food value from the fact that such huge creatures as the larger whales feed entirely upon it. This is enough to make it imperative to find out if we shall soon, or ever, be able to utilize plankton for human food or as substitute for our depleted acreage.

What kind of a crop is this which has thrived unnoticed at our doors since the beginning of man? In the first place, although the vegetable plankton alone is at the very base of the food chain, we are obliged to consider with it the small animal plankton, for in catching one we catch the other. One of the factors affecting the collection of plankton from the sea is its small size and the great variation in size between its different types. It is roughly classified from macroplankton, the largest kind, to nannoplankton, the most minute variety. An interesting lead in recent research originating from the British laboratory at Plymouth suggests strongly that the bulk of vegetable plankton may actually fall within the ultramicroscopic range in size of the nannoplankton. As for the animal plankton which feeds upon these other types, they vary from creatures several inches in diameter down to unicellular animals no larger than the small vegetable plankton. It is necessary to go into these distinctions in the size and types of plankton when we consider them as a potential crop. Obviously, from a technical standpoint, the removal from the sea of minute microorganisms much less than a thousandth of an inch long is quite a different problem from, let us say, the capture of the larger planktonic creatures such as jellyfish. That is why man, to date, has fed indirectly from the plankton pastures after they have been harvested for us by the fishes. But it is just this downgrading and waste of energy that we now aim to avoid. Let's take a look at some of the commoner and more useful kinds of these small plants and sea creatures.

The animal plankton or sea-grazers feed for the most part on planktonic vegetation known as diatoms. They are called diatoms because their thin silica shell, sculptured into many beautiful forms, is divided into two halves or valves. The slowly-sinking shells of these tiny diatoms over millions of years have formed large deposits of silica on the deep ocean floor. Today, where ocean bottom in past ages has been raised up as land, we mine this diatomaceous earth and use it for filters in various industries. While alive, these small plantlike atomies manage to float in the upper waters of the sea because of their delicate spiny shells which act as parachutes and because they contain buoyant droplets of oil in their bodies as a reserve food.

There is another very important group of vegetable plank-

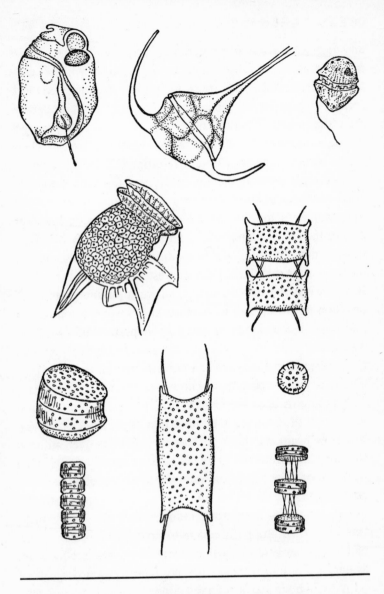

*Figure 15.* Permanent vegetable plankton. Dinoflagellates (above) and diatoms (below). Greatly magnified.

ton, also varied into many fantastic shapes, called the dino-flagellates because, unlike most other forms, they have two little whiplike antennae by which they propel themselves. Some of these have shells of cellulose and some of them are quite naked. When certain kinds of these occur in unusual abundance, they may poison and so discolor the ocean surface that we call it the "red tide." In the Gulf of Mexico, this phenomenon is responsible for the death of great numbers of fishes from time to time.

Probably almost everywhere the most numerous of all plankton is the infinitesimal nannoplankton which passes through the meshes of the finest nets. But under the microscope it can be seen that these forms have their individual structure, beauty and delicate organization. They are small, of much the same size as bacteria, but have incongruously ponderous names such as the prevalent coccolithophorids. They have rods and plates of limestone in their bodies and this, through the lengthy but descriptive scientific nomenclature, explains their name.

This brief look at the most important forms of the drifting vegetation gives only a passing glance at the variety of evolutionary experimentation in form and device to be found in the upper two hundred feet of the sunlit seas, but it is enough to indicate the nature of the principal population of its pastures: first, the diatoms which are most plentiful in the colder seas, then the dinoflagellates which are most numerous in the warmer waters and finally the tiny nannoplankton, most universally distributed but with a preference for warm waters.

Although we are principally concerned here with oceanic vegetation, something must be said of the equally small

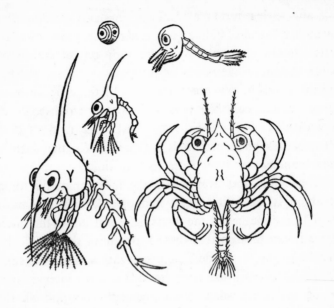

*Figure 16.* The young plankton stages of the European edible crab. Magnified.

___

zooplankton or animal plankton since it is impossible to harvest one variety without the other and the animal plankton are really the primary grazers. Unlike the vegetable world of the sea, the animal plankton of floaters and drifters, besides its permanent members, temporarily harbors the young of fishes and crustacea in their larval periods. Many things from young cod to newly born sponges or oyster spat come within this category until they reach a stage of development when they can provide their own locomotion or settle down as bottom-living adult creatures.

Some of the permanent animal plankton are almost as small as the plants. These are the protozoa, made of microscopic single cells. There are several varieties of these whose great abundance over millions of years during the geological upheavals of the earth have formed deposits on former ocean beds which now are part of the land. The foraminifera, for instance, with their lime shells formed the great chalk downs of southern England and other minute creatures, the radiolaria with shells of silica, have deposited an ooze and rock on the deep oceanic floors. Another group of important protozoans are the tintinnids with urnshaped shells firmly fixed to their bodies. These are largely found in coastal waters.

Among the larger floating population are creatures several inches in size, with some few much larger varieties, such as the jellyfish and the Siphonophores or bell-jellies. The largest jellyfish, which we have spoken of as refuge for small cod, may sometimes reach 6 feet in diameter with trailing tentacles a hundred feet long. Some of the most interesting of the strangely formed animal plankton are the arrow worms which are less than an inch or two in length but have terrible-looking jaws and are voracious feeders. They have proven a most important source of information in fishery research because they inhabit water masses of certain temperature and content and so have been used as indicators of the probable herring crop in the Channel and the North Sea. Most shellfish have planktonic periods only when they are in the larval stage but there are two groups of shellfish which live regularly in the plankton for their entire lives. These are called pteropods, or wing-feet and heteropods. More distantly related to them are the squids which only in smaller varieties are inactive enough to be considered plankton.

As an example of the strangely experimental forms evolution has produced within the sea there is a special group of organisms related to the vertebrates called salps. They are colonial organisms, that is, they group in chains of individuals sometimes several feet in length and have transparent coverings that are often beautifully colored and iridescent. Some of these, notably the Pyrosomas or fire-bodies, are extremely luminescent in the water. They are equipped with delicate mechanisms for sifting out with great efficiency the minute animal and vegetable plankton upon which they feed.

But in sheer number and variety the most important members of the zooplankton are the tiny crustacea or joint-legged shellfish. They are related to the crabs, lobsters and shrimp with which we are familiar. In fact, the larger non-planktonic edible crustacea, when small, assume forms quite unlike those which they have when mature and in this initial phase they, too, exist as plankton. Perhaps the most universally distributed of the permanent animal plankton are called copepods. They have jointed limbs, a single eye and long antennae with which they row through the water. They range from one-twenty-fifth to one-fifth of an inch in size. Because of their wide distribution they are one of the principal planktonic foods for herring and other plankton-eating fishes and sea animals. They form an important link with the vegetable plankton of the sea pastures since they are admirably equipped with hairlike growths on their limbs for sifting the minute plants from the water. So dominant are

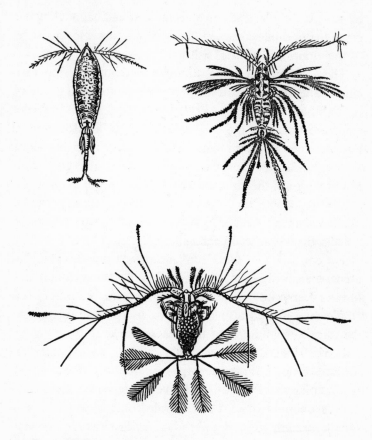

*Figure 17*. Various plankton copepods magnified.

these copepods as ocean grazers that they might well be compared in function in the oceanic food chain with the place held by cattle on land. They accumulate within their bodies vitamins and oils which small fishes in turn take in when they feed upon them and again pass on, through the herring, copelin and so forth, to the cod and haddock which come to our table. They are the original source, for instance, of the vitamin content of fish-liver oil.

There is another important small creature in the food chain called the euphausiid, which is shrimplike and known to the whale fishermen as krill. It is a familiar of the colder waters. Sometimes the euphausiids are brilliantly colored red and they all carry light organs within their inch-long bodies, but for the most part they are transparent and colorless. They form the chief diet of the huge whalebone whales, and it is possible that the ocean scientists' recent number one interest, the "scattering layer," which at varying depths reflects the impulse of echo-sounding, may be to a great extent composed of these euphausiids. At present this phenomenon is being studied intensively at the Miami University Marine Laboratory and elsewhere, both for its purely scientific interest and also because of its possible relation to the future exploitation of our sea resources.

Having looked at some of the plants and animals that form the crop of our sea acreage we can now turn to a rough quantitative survey of this ill-harvested resource. Its magnitude is undoubted, as a few simple comparisons with our farming wealth on land will show. For instance, it has been calculated that on the average an acre of sea produces three times the plant growth of a land acre. In the vast expanse of the sea about 135 billion tons of carbon are fixed, that is, incorporated by plant growth, to form 350 billion tons of starches annually. However, according to H. W. Harvey, it takes 300 grams of vegetable plankton to produce one gram of carnivorous fish and man only traps a fraction of these fish. Yet others have computed that, at the best, an acre of sea can produce 6,400 pounds of plankton per year, while on land production may reach, for corn, 5,720 pounds, oats 1,000 pounds and beef 800 pounds. Unfortunately, and here is our problem, because of a difficult environment, primitive harvesting, scattered crop, distant market and easily spoiled product, today we eat ten times more meat and fowl than we do fish.

These estimates of vegetation or of fish existing in the ocean give us an incomplete picture of the amount of food which is being produced. In the temperate and colder zones of the sea, where the waters are often discolored by the great quantities of drifting life contained, there is obviously a plankton crop of considerable size. And so it goes for the plankton feeders and for the fishes which live upon them in turn. We see great shoals of fishes and we measure with plankton nets large concentrations of plankton and so we estimate the crop. But in tropical seas such as the root of the Gulf Stream as it leaves the Caribbean or in the equatorial waters of the Pacific, we see clear blue water, transparent because of the dearth of suspended plankton. And to this, the measured calculations of the oceanographers bring confirmation of a low concentration, a poor crop. For such reasons it was long contended that the tropics are relative deserts, the colder zones relatively lush productive areas of the sea. In great measure these conclusions were true, but this is only half of the story.

We may look at the ocean crop at any one time as a series of steps in the pyramid. At the bottom is the vast quantity of vegetable plankton. Next above in order is the animal plankton, smaller in quantity since it grazes upon the microscopic plants. And so, in turn, we reach the highest and at the same time the smallest standing crop, the carnivorous fishes. But the true measure of yield depends upon dynamic changes continually taking place and to understand these we must replace our conception of a pyramid by one of intermeshing wheels. Put another way, it is the rate at which goods are replaced on the shelves, the turnover rather than the standing inventory which measures the business of a store. It is the rate at which plankton is being produced from mineral elements that counts and it is the rate at which plankton is converted to fish which measures the ocean yield for man. With these ideas in mind we see that the standing crop at any moment is the result of a complex balance of the food or mineral absorbed from the step below and of the material which is in turn removed by the grazing or predation of the step above.

We now have a different touchstone to apply to the potential wealth of the tropical seas. The rate at which animals and plants are able to live, to absorb food, to grow and in turn be absorbed by other steps of the food pyramid is greater in the tropics than elsewhere. The wheels are turning faster. The metabolic rate, the index of living, goes higher as the surroundings become warmer. In this and in other ways we begin to revise our ideas as to where and as to how much the sea may provide.

As we have seen in previous chapters, currents both vertical and horizontal bring nutrients to sea pastures and likewise renew or remove its populations, just as storms, sudden changes of temperature, overcrowding, overgrazing by herbivores and other factors affect the balance of the life cycle. It can be said "that the size of the standing crop at any time is the result of the summation of the excess of production over destruction from the beginning of the growth of the population to the moment of observation."

By following this scheme of measurement, only in a great deal more detail than we have attempted to indicate, a pretty good picture can be obtained of the possible yield at given places at sea, such, for instance, as studies made a few years ago at the famous Georges Banks. Gordon Riley has estimated, perhaps somewhat optimistically, that per acre per year about 20 tons of wet plankton produce about seven pounds of fish and that the actual world production of fish in all the seas each year is from one hundred to a thousand times the actual catch. But whether we talk in terms of vegetable plankton as the broad base of the food triangle or the herbivores as a second step, or the various sizes and degrees of the carnivorous fishes, the primary measure of the productivity of a sea area is still related, of course, to the quantities of living compounds it contains at a given time. Thus, the concentration of nutrient salts, or the measure of the rate of photosynthesis, or the rate of oxygen consumption or the utilization of phosphates—all provide some index to the production of the sea.

It is natural that the sea pasturage will vary in production, not only in mass but in kind, as the different influences we have just mentioned affect the vegetable and animal crops. For instance, where the Wyville Thompson Ridge makes an undersea barrier between Scotland and Iceland only 11 per cent of the life in the sea is common to both sides. This undersea wall helps divide the Atlantic and the Arctic waters. North of the Ridge the temperature of 4° C. is only 600 meters down, while south of the Ridge this temperature level is 1500 meters below the surface. Likewise, the temperature and water density in the tropics affects life in the sea. There, the standing crop of plankton is low but the metabolic rate is higher; not only this, but light penetrates deeper and the layer of vegetation is correspondingly thicker. And so the rate of production is higher. Such factors as these lead to the conclusion that there may be a much greater production, especially of nannoplankton, in tropical waters than has previously been thought.

Looking at the quantitative estimate of life in the oceans, we should be certain of a vast supply of food if harvesting and marketing techniques could be evolved through further research and so enable us to use it. Now we must take a look at the nutritional value of this supply and see what unknown, or at least unsolved, factors remain there. Studies have been made upon the nutritional value of various types of plankton in American waters, notably the Gulf of Maine, where the concentrations average about the same as in European waters. The catches were, as usual, mostly copepods but at times it was found that jellyfish, salps and seaworms dominated in the catch. One of the hazards to be met in using plankton as future source of food is this unpredictable variation in the catch which changes in season with shifting currents, and even between day and night. Likewise, there are certain species like the *Gonyaulax catenella* of the Pacific which are poisonous and which, when consumed by mussels, make them poisonous too. There is *Gymnodinium brevis* of the Gulf of Mexico, the Red Tide unicell which kills fishes. However, the general catch of plankton may be considered as potential food. Plankton was netted in coastal waters, waters of the continental slope and in the Sargasso Sea near Bermuda and was analyzed chemically for food value. The zooplankton in the coastal waters was four times as rich as that of the slope and sixteen times as rich as the Bermuda catches. This bears out the controlling effect of fertilizing nutrients which are usually richest near shores or banks. The plankton obtained in these experiments, when suitably dried, averaged as follows: about 55 per cent protein, about 4 per cent fat, about 25 per cent total ash and 15 per cent carbohydrates. This was after some of the sodium and chlorine salts had been washed out. There were also in these animals traces of phosphorus, potash, calcium, magnesium, sulfur, and certain vitamins and carotene. In other words, the elements of a well-rounded food.

Experiments were tried on feeding rats this straight sea product but with only slight success. They could not subsist on an unmixed diet. They could live for a considerable time on a mixture of plankton and meal. The general conclusion was that the rats could only use a fraction of the nutrients present in the plankton. This does not prove that man could not do better. The men on the Kon-Tiki raft ate plankton with no ill effects and it has been tried tentatively on humans elsewhere, but no fully controlled experiments with a plankton diet for man have yet been made.

But we do not have to rely on laboratory analysis alone in order to show the concentrated food value of plankton. Some of the greatest fishes and animals of the sea skip the various stages of downgrading of energy from the original planktonic source and feed directly on the minute creatures themselves. These are the basking sharks of the Hebrides and the antarctic whales. In an earlier chapter we mentioned the attempt to capture the huge sharks of western Scotland for their high-vitamin liver oil and to use their flesh as a food. These fish, which run up to 30 feet in length and weigh several tons. do not feed on other fishes, but sift the rich waters of the Hebrides for plankton. They cruise along the surface in the tideways at about two knots, and every day, when feeding, filter two thousands tons of water through their gaping jaws which are lined with hairlike leafy nets to trap the minute prey. Plankton is certainly good for them. Likewise, the huge whalebone whales grow prodigiously on a diet of krill where the antarctic waters are turbulent from convection currents which make a great upwelling from the ocean bottoms rich in nutrient. Professor A. C. Hardy, the authority on planktonic life, writes: "The great rorquals, the Blue and Fin whales, become sexually mature and reach an average length of 75 feet and 65 feet respectively in only two years from birth; they are born more than twenty feet long after some eleven months of foetal life. This prodigious mammalian growth, including the formation of great food reserves in the blubber, is built up entirely on a planktonic diet. It would certainly appear worthwhile to inquire if some of this wealth of food could not be taken directly from the sea to be used, if not for human consumption, as a valuable addition to the food of stock." Although this estimate of whale growth is now thought to be a little high, it gives a vivid idea of the food potency of plankton. Dr. George Clarke, who has done much plankton investigation on this side of the Atlantic, suggested the possibility of nets to catch the plankton located in tidal estuaries.

With a similar idea Hardy suggested an experimental station in the waters of the Hebrides whose rich plankton in past days fed whales and which still supports great schools of herring and the basking sharks. He advised a net made of stramin, a small-meshed fabric supported by longitudinal and transverse lengths of rope and with an opening 30 meters square. With a filtering efficiency of 20 per cent, which has proven feasible, this net could filter more than 22,000 tons of water per hour in a two-knot tide. In many places in the Scottish sea lochs such tides prevail twelve hours of the day. A reversal of the nets would clear them from clogging. Hardy estimated that ten such nets fishing twelve hours per day would yield more than 500 pounds dry weight of plankton. This could feed 357 people, provided of course they would eat it. He then pointed out that more than a thousand miles of drift nets were used by the British herring industry in its prime. One hundred fleets of ten tidal nets tended by a total of 200 men should, according to this estimate, yield 26 tons per day of dry plankton or enough food value for 37,500 people.

This may sound overly optimistic but Hardy, who invented the plankton counter for fishermen, is not only acquainted with the industry from the laboratory end but is familiar with the practice of commercial fisheries from long study. It is true, book estimates overlook the trial-and-error and practical difficulties which intervene between the idea and its commercial execution, but it is likewise true that as men become adept at any technique the original estimates of success are often far exceeded.

The question may well be asked, since the basking sharks and whales do all this so well, why not eat them after they have done the plankton harvesting for us? We have spoken of the difficulty of capturing and preparing for market the great sharks. Gavin Maxwell covers this in his fascinating

account of his own try. Also, we are well aware that the
great whale fleets of highly mechanized vessels already
threaten the supply of those animals in antarctic waters and
elsewhere. The reproduction of these leviathans is slow, and
unable to keep pace with the rate at which we should like to
catch them. We have not begun, yet, to take full advantage
of modern advances in the various fields of engineering in
applying them to the mechanics of a new plankton fishery.
But already we foresee rapid development of plankton indicators, samplers and electronic detectors based upon echo-
sounding for seeking areas where plankton predominates.
The Rockefeller Foundation and other important organizations have already noted the vital part of plankton and the
role it plays in the ocean economy and they are today actively
supporting basic research in this field at various centers of
oceanographic research.

Based on the experience of fish farming in enclosed or
semi-enclosed waters, proposals have been made for the
cultivation of plankton under the direct control of man.
This certainly provides food, if only for thought, but at
present it holds out little practical hope as a means of increasing protein foods from the sea. An example that somewhat parallels this idea is already being pushed with vigor
on land in the artificial propagation under ideal conditions
of fresh-water algae, notably *Chlorella*. At present the
principal interest of the much discussed *Chlorella* experiments is the fact that in a laboratory-factory the environment
of the plant growth can be controlled to advantage by man.
For instance, in hydroponic agriculture the plants live in
water plus nutrients in fixed containers or tanks with the

temperature and even the composition of the atmosphere under exact controls.

As a result of increasing studies of photosynthesis carried on by the Carnegie Institute, by Stanford University and in other research laboratories, the idea is gaining that unicellular algae such as *Chlorella* could possibly be developed on a large scale as a protein source. In order to understand this we must know that these algae also are a direct source of protein, running over 50 per cent. As chemical factories they are able to absorb the energy of the sun and turn it into food with an efficiency of as high as 2 per cent against 0.1 per cent in ordinary vegetation, and this is almost entirely useful, with none of the waste matter found in our accustomed leafy vegetables.

It goes without saying that the world needs this kind of a substitute for meat proteins. It takes fifty times as much land to make the same number of calories for beef as for sugar beets. It is readily seen as our population races ahead of feasible expansion of our land pastures for high protein foods that man must turn to a vegetable diet where soybean fats can replace butter, and fish, algae and other protein substitutes replace what would have to be an impossibly large and relatively inefficient expansion of meat. But it is not as simple as it sounds.

Before these encouraging laboratory experiments with *Chlorella* will be of any use to man, much more research and skillful technological developments are needed. As Dr. Spoehr of the Carnegie Institute rightly warns: "The problem of food supply is as old as man himself . . . the grimness and formidable proportions of this problem are causing concern to even this, the most favored of nations. The food problem is above all a practical one, practical in the sense that contributions towards its solution must ultimately demonstrate actual usefulness within the medium of present day society. This . . . presenting almost innumerable economic, politico-social, practical and scientific problems . . . is the meeting ground for many disciplines." At present we know that *Chlorella* reproduces itself under ideal conditions with great rapidity. It can double its cell structure in a day. It can be fed optimum nutrients and be kept in an atmosphere of carbon dioxide many times that available in the open air. In a word, it can be nursed to produce higher food value per unit of land than any crop man has yet devised, but at great expense. Until, as Dr. Spoehr so wisely indicates, this can meet quantity requirements at attractive competitive prices in a palatable form it is merely romance to state that in algal culture we have the solution of the world food hunger ready at hand. The hopeful beginning has been made. But much money, brains and time are still needed to solve this problem. This fascinating story of *Chlorella* must only be briefly touched upon here but its consideration is necessary to emphasize the much greater difficulties facing man in algae and plankton culture in the seas, where further research may well unearth cultivatable forms with even more desirable characteristics than *Chlorella*.

A sort of plankton farming, one step removed, has actually been attempted in salt water, where plankton growth was artificially encouraged as a food for fish crops. The most notable experiment along these lines was undertaken at Loch Sween on the west coast of Scotland. Fertilizers of nitrates and phosphates were directly added to the small lochs. At first the results were most encouraging. The pasturage of phytoplankton and bottom growth both increased enormously, except when a like increase in animal plankton kept the vegetable plankton down by excessive grazing. But it became clear that much of the fertilizer was absorbed without giving its full return of plankton. But here we are for the moment interested in the rapid, controlled reproduction of vegetable plankton in the sea. It is obvious there can be no such careful supervision or control as with *Chlorella* on the land. Factors of temperature, currents, the presence of grazing zooplankton, the precipitation and absorption of fertilizer to the bottom muds and other phenomena natural to semi-open waters are not easily eliminated. But one lead from the experiments in plankton culture in partially enclosed areas gives hope for the development of techniques and that is the ability of the minute vegetation to rapidly make use of fertilizers added by man. Harvey has estimated that the sea averages a thousand pounds of animal tissue per acre—all basically dependent on phytoplankton—and that this quantity might be stepped up to a phenomenal extent, compared to any like increase in cattle culture on land, if we could devise the means for controlling the food chain. In time we may move from hunting fish to farming fish, and then to the highly desirable but remoter techniques of a man-controlled sea agriculture of applied fertilizers and efficient harvesting. *Chlorella* culture on land and the breeding of plankton in marine laboratories has assured us of this possibility, but at present an effective harvest of protein from the great sea pastures must wait on careful and co-ordinated research which is still in its infancy.

Meanwhile, there are other possibile uses of this planktonic wealth as a basic transferring medium of the sun's radiation. If we pursue man's uses of natural resources, we find that in one way or another all forms of energy, whether food or fuel or other kinds of power, are phases of the sun's radiation.

# CHAPTER 7

# Atom, Sun and Sea

SO FAR, WE HAVE BEEN LOOKING AT the sea as a source of a fresh and increased food supply for our rapidly growing land populations. We have attempted to outline the many difficulties of the ocean environment and the necessity of a great expansion of man's activity in research and invention before the undoubted wealth of the oceans, as yet only in fractional production, can be made available to mankind at large. We have so far thought of this latent energy continually reproducing itself in fish or in ocean pasturage in terms of food. But it also could be a direct or indirect way of increasing power supplies for our complex and mechanized modern civilization to furnish heat and light, to drive the wheels of factories, and for transporting us by auto, train, airplane and steamship. But we should not look at our world energy resources in separate compartments. We must consider the problem as a whole, for what we must seek in the unexploited frontier of the sea is measured by the present and future use and rapid depletion of our land resources.

Man as a naked beast spends much of his time protecting himself from the weather. Aboriginal man could do little else than adapt himself to the world as he found it. He was few in numbers and his days were brief compared to modern man who has created an artificial environment and a higher or, at least, a more mechanized and physically more comfortable standard of living. As a result, our greatest single energy requirement outside of the food we consume is that spent on heating our houses and other kinds of habitation. In the United States alone a quarter of all our fuel is used for space heating and in less industrialized countries the percentage for this runs higher. We have in the past fifty years become a continent on wheels and, as a result, an additional one-eighth of all the energy released in the United States goes to keeping our automobiles hurrying from place to place. The other five-eighths of our total pool of power goes into railroads, planes, industrial machinery, chemical plants and electric generation. In terms of energy our standard of living is very costly in the use of natural resource. In some countries, which are still on the borders of an industrial way of life, as much as nine-tenths of the energy requirement is for heating and only one-tenth needed for other purposes. In one form or another the world today is using about 5 billion horsepower and the United States alone consumes a fifth of this total.

What are the sources of this energy we are using? Man is indeed a child of the sun, for we must look to the sun as a great nuclear reactor for almost all of the energy of our daily use. The nature of this nuclear reaction is the conversion of hydrogen atoms into helium atoms, which releases the beneficent rays of the sun. A fraction of this sunlight, striking our earth in the past, has been stored in our fossil fuels. Today, it recreates the immediate vegetable and ani-

mal life around us. The recent discovery of how to avail ourselves of radioactive energy from some of our minerals has
led to the prodigious energy concentration of the atom bomb.
Also, fortunately, great expectations have been aroused
and a good deal of research inaugurated towards channeling
this new release of energy into peaceful and civilized industrial uses. But all this energy still remains an expendable
source with foreseeable limits.

We need not mine, of course, the sun's radiant energy.
We have always found it in the form of vegetation which in
earlier civilizations has been adequate for wood fuel in
heating, cooking and for simple industries. But this, at one
time apparently inexhaustible and renewable source of
energy, has reached its limits in the face of the expanded
needs of an explosive increase of world population in the
modern industrial age. As our frontiers of unexploited resource contracted, supplies of wood became locally inadequate and we reached for coal and then for oil, both of
which are merely vegetable fossils and therefore just as
much a product of solar energy trapped by photosynthesis
as are living trees or wood when consumed as fuel. But oil
and coal are minerals. They are not renewable. The origin
of coal lies in the petrified wood of ancient swamps and
jungles whereas the source of oil is the remains of sea vegetation, of planktonic plants and animals trapped in the
sediments of ancient seas during the successive ages when
the oceans overlay land masses, sediments which later rose
into the air again as our present continents.

Let us quote here briefly from *The Ocean River*. "The
origin of oil-bearing rocks, the precise alchemy of nature
that transformed the original remains of plants and animals

into oil, and the ways in which this oil became concentrated in its underground reservoirs are still not fully understood, despite the great economic importance of the problem and the considerable amount of scientific research that has been devoted to it over the past century. Nevertheless, the problem is gradually yielding to investigation, and we may be fairly sure of the broad outlines if not the details of these infinitely slow processes that bring us fuel and energy from the past.

"Between the great mountain-building periods, when branches and eddies of the Ocean River circulated over the continents, the future oil-bearing sediments were laid down in the shallow seas. Trapped in the mud and sands of the sediments, the dead bodies of plants and animals that lived and died in the waters above were gradually buried under the thousands of feet of rock, where a long series of chemical changes converted them to petroleum. Strangely enough, it is not from fishes, giant reptiles, voracious squids, and belemnites that we believe the foundations of today's oil fields began. It is much more probable that the bulk of these organic materials in the oil-breeding muds of the ancient sea-floor came from very much smaller varieties of life.

"Though small, sometimes even invisible to the naked eye, this drifting life of the plankton many times exceeds in bulk the entire mass of fishes, clams, crustacea and other obvious creatures, even though these may individually be thousands of times larger. The energy of sunlight, trapped by the minute plants of the plankton, is used through the green magic of their chlorophyll to build up within their tissues, from the everpresent carbon dioxide dissolved in water, the chemical foodstuffs we call carbohydrates. The teeming microscopic plants of the plankton and the infinite numbers of small planktonic animals that feed upon them have lived their short lives, and their dead bodies have rained ceaselessly down upon the sea-floors throughout the entire history of the fossil sediments, carrying with them the sun's energy transformed into this chemical energy of the carbohydrates. As they became buried in the accumulating sediments their bodies decayed and their substance was converted into the starting materials from which petroleum was formed.

"This process did not take place in the ancient sea-floors. Parker Trask, Claude ZoBell, and others, from their investigations of modern sediments have given us some insight into the nature of these deposits. It seems fairly certain now that oil was mainly formed from plankton remains in the sediments of shallow seas. This was especially true when these seas became partly cut off from the main ocean, just as part of the great ancestral gulfs of North America and of Tythys, the ancient Mediterranean, were sometimes cut off from the North Atlantic basin. It seems probable too that, just as today the bottom waters of the Black Sea are lacking in oxygen as a result of conditions set up by its isolation, so were the waters of some of those bygone inland seas.

"Under ordinary conditions the organic remains in sediments are oxidized and their chemical energy is lost, so that they are no longer able to change into oil-producing materials. In the Black Sea today, though, due to lack of oxygen there is a great increase of bacteria of a special type, and it these reducing bacteria that bring about a chemical transmutation in the deposits. One effect of this alchemy is to make the bottom waters poisonous to other forms of life; but another effect is to start the sediments along the long chemical road which leads to petroleum. The same lack of oxygen that is believed to be so important in the early development of oil-producing sediments is also found in some of the limestone muds forming today beneath the waters of the River as they circulate in the Gulf of Mexico. Francis Shepard, submarine geologist of the Scripps Institute of Oceanography, and his associates, have begun a detailed study of such deposits in the western part of the Gulf, and the limestone sediments around the Florida Keys are being studied by marine scientists at The Marine Laboratory in Miami. It is likely that these studies of the sea floor will throw new light on the ancient alchemy that brought oil to the sediments of a hundred million years ago."

Today man has already explored other means of obtaining fuel from living vegetation, for he is well aware of the rapid depletion of his fossil fuels. The driving energy for our machines may be obtained both from wood and other vegetation. For instance, sugar beets and agricultural wastes are transformed by means of fermentation into alcohol and others are made into gasoline by the chemical conversion of the Fischer-Tropsch process.

What we are looking for always, however, is the most direct method of trapping solar energy, and beginnings have been made along these lines such as the use of heat collectors in solar water heaters which are so frequently used in homes in Florida and California. New types of heat storage devices are also under development. At present our attempts to concentrate the sun's rays sufficiently to heat boilers and run machinery are still very much in the experimental stage, and so are the various kinds of research underway to convert sunlight into electrical energy by photoelectric processes and by photochemical reactions. Similar lines of experiment are those of various groups of scientists, working to duplicate photosynthesis in the laboratory outside of the living cell.

More familiar forms of solar energy put to human use are the windmill and the use of waterpower. Though the connection may not seem obvious, they are a part of the engine of solar power derived from the furnace of the sun through convection, or the unequal heating of the air. This effect brings about great movements which are seen in our permanent wind systems, governed in their motions by seasonal changes as the earth rolls in its orbit around the sun. We can watch the power of the winds on sailing vessels and the windmills which pump water and charge storage batteries.

The power of the sun is transformed into waterpower in this way. About a third of the total energy of the sun falling upon the globe hits the surface of the seas, lakes and rivers and the rain-soaked lands. By evaporation it lifts the invisible water vapor against gravity up into the atmosphere. This energy is so immense that it amounts to twenty thousand times all the power used by man today. But of this great expenditure of energy over 99 per cent is used simply to evaporate the water. When the vapor condenses again into clouds and rain and snow, there is a great release of the trapped heat of vaporization and this is lost by radiation into space.

Due to the uneven conformation of the land and the distance the rain has to travel before it courses down from

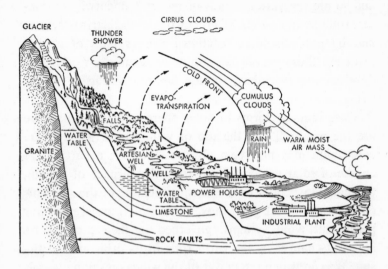

*Figure 18.* Diagram showing transformation of solar energy into water power. Water evaporates from sea and land to form clouds. These release rain. Part of the rainfall is held by the soil. Part enters underground reservoirs. The remainder runs off into falls, lakes and rivers from which it may be diverted into plants for generating electrical power.

mountains to the level plains and the sea, we are able to convert some of the work done by the sun in raising the water masses against the force of gravity. We impound water behind dams, where in response to the force of gravity it drives our hydroelectric plants on its way to the sea.

In addition to these forms of the sun's energy, which we can recapitulate as that trapped in fossil coal and oil, in the living plants, or converted to winds and waterfalls, or used more directly in solar heaters or finally through the chemical or electrical equivalents of photosynthesis, there are three other sources of energy available to us on land. We have already mentioned that of nuclear fission. Another is the internal heat of the earth which we see in volcanic action and geysers as a reminder that beneath the solid crust we tread is a great central furnace. This type of energy has been put to work to good effect in Italy where it furnishes power for industrial purposes. Unfortunately, for various reasons the availability of this kind of power is geographically very limited. The third form of energy is the earth's rotation which acts as a giant flywheel upon which we live.

Naturally, all these sources of energy are not equally available for our use. In looking at our present and future needs we find that coal and oil and natural gas which constitute our fossil fuels, make up 92 per cent of the energy which we use today. This is not a happy inventory, for in these we live off capital resource which is nonrenewable and which, once expended, is gone forever. These fuels took millions of years to accumulate and today mankind is using them up so fast that they will be completely gone in a few hundred years. Meanwhile, we let our populations run wild in mounting numbers which can only accentuate this reckless expenditure of the bounties of the earth. If our rate of industrial development and its corresponding use of energy goes on increasing, as it has done during the first half of the twentieth century, the end of our major source of energy comes very close upon us. Moreover, long before our coal and oil are finished, in fact in the immediate future, the pinch of dwindling supply will be felt and we will be forced to the more difficult and uneconomic use of low-grade sources which we would once have discarded. Our

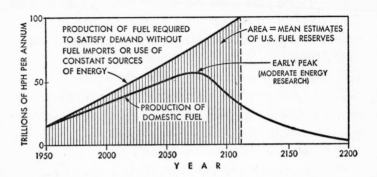

*Figure 19.* Future of power if based on coal and oil alone. The pinch would start in 2075 A.D. and the end would arrive in 2200 A.D.

concern here is not directly with these estimates of the time remaining, but only to show that such a time has its foreseeable limits.

So we are faced with a future in which coal and oil have been of use to us only for a brief moment in the history of mankind to give life-blood to our industrial civilization. Where can we look beyond this for a new transfusion of energy from sources not fully exploited; not a temporary reprieve but a permanent and continuously renewable access to the sun's energy? At the moment, of course, the exciting prospect of nuclear fission comes to mind. Aside from our immediate concern with the death-dealing nature of this new source of energy, we do happily know that we can build reaction piles which can be turned to ordinary commercial uses. And yet there are reasons why we cannot look with unreserved optimism upon atomic fission as a complete escape from our dependence upon coal and oil.

For nuclear fuel, uranium is, like coal and oil, a non-renewable resource and once it has undergone the transformation of fission its usefulness is gone for good. Moreover, fissionable uranium as an ore is rare and in low concentrations. Ordinary nonfissionable uranium may be converted to a fissionable metal, plutonium, in a nuclear reaction pile. This process is known as "breeding" and makes possible an increase in our supply of nuclear fuel by using the more common uranium isotope. There are other possibilities, such as the conversion of thorium, which is more abundant than uranium, to a fissionable atom. But all of these methods work within the inescapable limitation that nuclear fuels, like coal and oil, are finite and expendable. They are the bounty of a geological upheaval that, were it repeated, would scarcely be of use to the present race of man.

The future resources of uranium have been estimated by experts and a calculation shows that their usefulness for producing power would not be more than about one-sixth of our total coal reserves. This does not help us too much. But to the extent that the "breeding" reactor can be used to convert ordinary thorium and uranium to atomic fuel, this total could be greatly increased, even, some think, to the equivalent of twenty-five times the coal reserves. The possibilities arising out of the "hydrogen bomb," though great, are unrelated to most peaceful uses of power and they scarcely fall within the scope of our present consideration.

There is no doubt that practical power plants operated by this new and plentiful atomic power will be in operation within ten years. The first atom-propelled submarine is already here. But there are certain limitations. These power plants may eventually be able to operate more cheaply than coal-fired plants, provided that we do not take into account the prodigious cost and enormous plants needed to obtain atomic fuel in the first place. It is not surprising then to realize that all in all more energy has already gone into producing atomic power than has been produced from it.

The more than two billion dollars already expended on atomic energy, if devoted to research into photosynthesis or into direct solar heat uses, would probably have brought about equally practical results and of a permanently renewable nature. Atomic energy, even though its reserves are considerably more than those of coal, will one day be finished—the evil day is merely pushed so far into the future that we lose immediate interest. But there still remain the limitations that the necessity for shielding the atomic motor prevents the use of small and portable units, in which so much of our power is used today. The problem of radioactive wastes in the manufacture of atomic fuel is an even greater one. There is no question but that atomic fission holds a bright future for mankind, if harnessed to peaceful purposes, but in the near future its uses will be limited and in the long run the ultimate limitation remains that it is nonrenewable and, unlike the direct energy of the sun, it cannot be considered a continuous resource for man.

Before returning to the basic energy of the vegetable world let us consider for a moment the possible future expansion of hydroelectric power and then the winds, as sources of solar energy. Since most of the rain falls into the sea or on the soil or forms streams too small or with insufficient fall to be useful, only a fractional part of water energy can be used at places where it can be impounded at useful altitudes. It is unlikely that all the streams can be used, so the most reasonable estimate of what we can develop during the next hundred years is about one billion horsepower and this is about one-fifth of our present energy needs. It will not replace coal and oil at the rate we use them. But even this estimate is about twenty times our present output. It will help, certainly, but there is no total solution here to the problem of energy requirements.

The use of wind power is old and accustomed but has increasingly attracted the attention of engineers and today it is regarded as perfectly possible to harness the wind to drive large turboelectric generators. But it is not practical to do so except in winds that blow between 20 to 30 miles per hour. Since steady winds at these velocities are found in only a few places, and in most parts of the world they vary greatly and are frequently outside these limits, it does not seem likely that wind power will ever be of more than local importance. For instance, today the wind batteries and windmill pumps of the United States generate an average rate of 54,000 horsepower. In comparison to this the energy used to drive only our electric fans throughout the land, with their little cooling winds, runs as high as 200,000 horsepower. It is obvious the wind is not the answer.

Although we must keep in mind the great potentials of atomic energy, a study of our expendable and nonrenewable sources of power on earth inevitably leads back to the delicate machinery of the plant as a possible answer to a continuous and permanent means of driving an expanding industrialized civilization. But when we turn to land plants for replenishable energy we are immediately faced with the problem that land turned to the uses of vegetation for fuel must be counted out as farmland available for human food. It is true that much land, useless for food crops, will grow trees of a kind which can be converted to fuel for driving machines. But, on the whole, there is no real answer in this to the inevitable end of coal and oil as fuel. Aside from heat and motive power, more and more we are turning to petroleum and coal products for materials for clothing, building and for plastics which replace materials formerly obtained from wood and other vegetation. This, in a small way, has released land for food use. But when coal and oil are gone—and these new uses hasten that end—we cannot go back to vegetation for fuels and materials at the expense of food production. The industrial uses of plant life must always remain dependent on and accessory to first satisfying the rising demand for food. This is easily realized when we consider that, if we used all the food crops of the United States and processed them by chemical means for fuel, it would not give us a sufficient supply to operate half of our present number of automobiles. We could, of course, using expensive and uneconomical methods, increase from three to six times our present fuel supply from vegetation, but that would leave no room for increasing our food supplies. In a word, there is an equivalence between food energy and industrial energy which cannot be ignored by those who forecast great new agricultural expansion as a solution to the food problem. It begs the question of the equally vital energy shortage that lies before us.

If, for instance, we used all the vegetation on earth which absorbs sunlight and converted it to chemical energy of one kind or another, it would provide us with some 6,000 million horsepower, or a little more than our total needs, but in thus using it we would have to deprive ourselves of all our land food. So we are forced to look to the vegetation of the sea for food or energy. Vegetable plankton is able to use sunlight more efficiently than land plants and taken as a whole it is estimated it can convert sunlight to chemical energy at the rate of 50,000 million horsepower, or about eight times that of our land growth. Since we use so little of the ocean's vast supply, even indirectly, for food we must give it serious consideration as a source of fuel.

In a previous chapter we took up the difficulties of harvesting this planktonic sea pasturage. But in spite of this, the importance of the energy shortage that lies ahead of us, as well as of our immediate food problem, should spur us on to make every effort towards satisfactory means of ultimately harvesting the sea as we do the land. Plankton and seaweeds, for instance, being rich in carbohydrates could be converted by hydrolysis and fermentation into alcohol, or, better still, by the Fischer-Tropsch process into petroleum fuel. At present, as our economy is set up, this would be too expensive but the need will come with increasing costs of fossil fuels and further research, and technological development may one day make this a practical possibility.

When we talked of plants as a source of food, we mentioned as a basic handicap that they use only one-tenth of 1 per cent of the sun's radiation. This low efficiency turned research to special forms of algae or rootless vegetation such as *Chlorella* which converts up to 2 per cent of the sun's radiation. *Chlorella* culture, even though only in the laboratory stage, is as far ahead of hydroponics or the chemical culture of ordinary food plants, as that process is ahead of old-fashioned agriculture. Algae culture under the careful control of man is therefore of special significance when we turn to vegetation as a source of fuel energy to replace fossil fuels. *Chlorella* may be raised in an atmosphere of carbon dioxide as high as 5 per cent, compared to the ordinary atmosphere with a mere 0.008 per cent and so can be more productive. But this is not the only advantage of algae production, as Scarlott points out: "*Chlorella* production can be carried out as a perfectly continuous industrial process, in which the irradiated suspension is filtered to remove developed algae, the mother liquor is fortified with make-up nutrient salts, the rate of flow of the suspension is controlled by the amount of the available solar energy and the concentration of carbon dioxide, and temperatures are maintained at optimum points. In this case the farm is a factory." He then adds that because of the infinite variety of phytoplankton an immense opportunity lies before the marine biologists in searching out possible ocean planktonic growths that are composed predominantly of carbohydrates. The adjoining table of yields compares various land and sea crops which are now available to us and clearly illustrates the rich field for scientific research that lies ahead in plant culture both on land and from the sea.

Ayres and Scarlott put the case for research in photosynthesis as a source of industrial energy as follows: "Those that know most about vegetation are inclined to believe that the best that technology will be able to do in the decades ahead will be to supply a sufficient amount of food for the two and a half billion people of the earth. The rate of increase of 1950 is about 60,000 per day, and we are starting this race well behind the mark. Tremendous progress will have to be made to catch up with events, and until this essen-

## TABLE II

### PERMANENT ENERGY SOURCES OF THE WORLD

RATE OF AVAILABILITY OR USE
(*In millions of HP*)

| SOURCE | RATE OF USE (1950) | MAXIMUM AMOUNT AVAILABLE IN THEORY | MAXIMUM USE POSSIBLE IN 100 YEARS' TIME |
|---|---|---|---|
| *Temporary* | | | |
| Coal and Oil | 4,600 | nonrenewable | nonrenewable |
| Nuclear Fission | negligible | nonrenewable | nonrenewable [1] |
| *Permanent Solar* | | | |
| Sea plants | negligible | 60,000 | ? |
| Land plants | 350 | 6,000 | 0 |
| Direct solar power | negligible | 2,000,000 | 2,500 |
| Direct solar space heat | negligible | as much as needed | 150 |
| Heat pumps | negligible | 200 | 20 |
| Water power | 50 | 40,000 | 300 |
| Wind | negligible | 200 | negligible |
| Sea heat | none | 2,000 | ? |
| *Permanent Nonsolar* | | | |
| Tides | negligible | 25,000 | 5 |
| Earth heat | negligible | 1,500 | negligible |
| | | | 2,975 plus energy from the ocean |
| TOTAL | 5,000 | | |

[1] but ample for some purposes for several thousand years

tial problem is solved we can see no peace on earth. For energy we will have to be content with 'scraps' unless, in-indeed, photosynthesis can be industrialized."

One of the advantages of the industrial production of algae in factory-laboratories is well illustrated by the fact that the waste carbon dioxide from industrial uses based upon the Fischer-Tropsch conversion of algae could be used again immediately to fortify the artificial atmosphere of the plant growth. Another important phase of research in increasing production efficiency along the lines of artificial photosynthesis is now being carried out at various universities and by an institution especially set up for the purpose by Charles Kettering, perhaps in atonement for what he has done to increase automobile uses of energy. The best we can do at present is to double this efficiency by using *Chlorella* instead of ordinary vegetation. In theory photosynthesis might be raised to the point of trapping 20 per cent of solar energy. But this would be accomplished only by setting aside the practical problems involved in supplying energy. This must be not only abundant but cheap. Speaking before the American Academy for the Advancement of Science Dr. Farrington Daniels had this to say: "There is no assurance that photosynthesis outside the living plant will be any better or cheaper than the present photosynthesis in plants. We are just beginning to understand something about the mechanism of photosynthesis. With all the millions of dollars invested in agricultural research, it is strange that so little has gone into the fundamental process of photosynthesis which underlies all agriculture."

There is a final and more direct method of using solar energy and this is the development of heat first-hand from the sun's rays using mirrors and traps to concentrate them and boilers to operate turbines for power. Hottel at The Massachusetts Institute of Technology figures that about

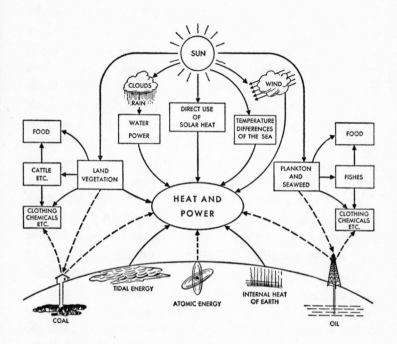

*Figure 20.* The sun is our main source of renewable energy. Temporary or non-renewable sources connected by dotted lines.

50 horsepower per acre might be trapped under the optimum conditions of the Arizona desert on an average annual basis. This adds up to about 400,000 horsepower-hours per annum per acre, which is about double that possible from vegetation if used for fuel and about seven times as efficient if the fuel were used to generate power. Carrying these fascinating figures ahead, on paper, and supposing the optical machinery were both economical and feasible to build, all

the heat and power now used in the United States could be obtained from an area of 50,000 square miles or about two-fifths of the State of New Mexico. In other words, in the future, after much more research and with good luck man can trap all the energy he needs from the sun at the price of enormous capital investment. Meanwhile people breed without control and they refuse to die amiably of starvation even though blessed by dogma. Certainly some more immediate sources of energy to serve this multitude must be eventually evolved. And here the answer is atomic energy. For the distant and permanent future, however, we must look to the sun. In doing this, the difficulty lies in how best to use the sunlight that falls upon the earth, and we cannot forget that the greater part falls on the sea and its vast green pasturage. Solar-heat engines will undoubtedly be useful one of these days but the fact remains that a very considerable source of unused solar energy lies before us in the floating vegetable world of the oceans and that the use of this would not interfere with other uses of the land.

At some stage in the future of the human race we shall have no choice but to use one or both of these sources. Either one of them will require a great amount of research and development.

# CHAPTER 8

# Sea Water
# Power Plants

WE HAVE DISCUSSED VEGETATION AS a source of energy common to land and sea and also the various forms of direct solar energy which may one day be called upon to solve the problem of the approaching days of power scarcity. It now remains to look at sources of power which exist in the sea alone, the ocean's own special kinds of powerhouse.

Man is the inhabitant of a huge flywheel that was given its powerful cosmic spin at the time of creation. This spin is energy, the energy of rotation of which we are aware in the winds and the tides. The gravitational pull of the moon merely guides and times the rhythm of the tidal movements of the seas, and in this the sun plays a minor controlling part. The source of power for these movements, however, comes from the rotational momentum of the earth. It is not received from outer space, and is independent of the direct energy of the sun which we have recently been discussing. But here we are only concerned with tidal energy because of its possible use to man as a source of power.

If we could only harness all the power of the tides with their daily and constant repetition, we could supply half of the four billion horsepower which the world needs, but this, of course, is impossible. Only a fraction of the ever-present surge of the seas can be of any use to us because of practical difficulties. Nevertheless, for a long time man has tried to engineer means of trapping some of it. Our colonial ancestors in the United States had tidal mills. Ayers and Scarlott report a small one still driving a sawmill in Maine. As a matter of fact, the first water-pumping station for the city of London came from a tidal millwheel built into old London Bridge, and this was still in operation as late as the early nineteenth century.

The basic pattern of useful devices for harnessing the flood and the ebb of the tide is the construction of dams provided with gates which catch and hold the flood tide. The water is then released through turbines or waterwheels to generate power at the ebb. The natural limitations of available coastal basins of sufficient size in areas where tides have a considerable rise are obvious and make it plain why we have not made more general use of this relatively simple means of trapping a constant and reasonably perpetual energy source.

Perhaps we should, for a moment, pause to consider how permanent tidal power is likely to be. Obviously, if we drive machinery from a flywheel, the energy taken from it will slow the wheel down, unless of course new power is supplied to keep up the rate of revolution. A familiar children's toy illustrates this. The yoyo has stored energy due to its rotation. Power from this is sufficient to roll it upwards along the string against gravity, but as it rises it slows down, in direct proportion to the energy expended. And so the rotation of the earth causes tidal movements and these dissipate energy in overcoming friction as the water is dragged across the face of the earth. The power used up in tidal movement may seem great to us, but compared to the vast energy stored up in the spinning of the earth it is small. So the two billion horsepower used up by tidal movement has slowed down the earth's rotation so little that, since the birth of Christ the day has become a mere two seconds longer. Thus, we may consider this power source a permanent one, so far as the human race is concerned.

Before discussing modern large-scale projects for using tidal energy we can take a look at the basic engineering principle upon which they all depend. The single basin plan is the most elementary. This operates where a tidal estuary or narrow inlet opens into a basin. A dam is thrown across the stream and as the tides rise, its gates are opened and then closed when the maximum level has been reached at the flood. When the tide is low or at the ebb the water is released through hydraulic turbines of some sort and power is generated until the beginning of the next flood or intake, or until the head of water impounded is too low to be useful. This requires a stoppage of the turbines while the impounded head of water is again being built up and is naturally inefficient to the extent of the interruption. It gives two periods of power generation per day but even these are not constant because of the shifting tidal periods, so there is little control of peak load in relation to the needs of those depending on this power for light or industrial purposes. There is no firm power.

To overcome this handicap a two-basin system was designed where the basins are separated from each other by a dam with gates, and each separate basin has its own gate to the sea. Here one basin is operated as a high-level basin and one as a low-level basin. The turbines are located at the gate between the two basins and operated to discharge at will, either into the sea or into the low-level basin. By timing of the use of the gates a flow of continuous power is now made possible. Firm or steady power thus available, however, is conditioned by a sacrifice in peak power and therefore of total power production, and also by the variability of the very low or neap tides. This can be overcome by pumping in sea water during periods of maximum generation as an adjunct to the fluctuating tidal action. This supplementary water can be used when the head is low. The continuous power thus generated is dependent on available storage area and, because it requires an expenditure of energy, it naturally reduces the net total of the power produced by the action of the sea.

There are not many places along our coasts that meet the requirements of storage basins in areas of a marked rise and fall in the tides. A minimum of a 10 foot tide is called for to make this kind of generation of power practical from an economic standpoint and even this is open to doubt. It is better to settle for a 20 foot difference in tidal range. In the United States, the Maine shores above Penobscot Bay best provide such conditions, notably at Passamaquoddy. The Hudson River might perhaps qualify as well. On the Pacific coast nowhere except in Alaska are conditions right.

Ayers and Scarlott, in their book on *Energy Sources* sum up the world situation for tidal power as follows: "Only about half a dozen of the world's major potential tide-power sites have received serious attention. These are the Severn River in southern England, the Rance River and Mont St. Michel on the shores of Brittany in northern France, the San José and Deseado Rivers of the Argentine, the Petitcodiac and Memramcook Estuaries in the Bay of Fundy, Canada, and the Passamaquoddy where Maine joins New Brunswick. If all of these sites were utilized to their fullest capacity, we might obtain about 0.2 per cent of the world's present energy requirement."

In spite of the fact that the Passamaquoddy project was initiated in the 1920's and got as far as a survey stage during the 1930's, the present power requirements of Great Britain coupled with a rapid dwindling of coal availability makes the project to dam the Severn the most likely one to be exploited in the near future. Due to the geographic nature of the Severn estuary into which the Bristol Channel funnels, this would have to be the single-basin type of development. But even with this obvious handicap there is enough variation in levels—between 47 feet maximum and 22 feet at the neap—to make it practicable under the circumstances.

Government studies favor a dam just above the confluence of the Severn and the Wye Rivers. This basin would fill during the incoming tides, twice daily, and when the head of 5 feet is reached on the ebb, the waters impounded would pour out through thirty-two 25,000 kilowatt generators until the head at the next flood tide became less than five feet, when the operation would cease until the basin was once more recharged with water. It is hoped that if this project is built, a flow of firm power could be reached by coordinating this variable supply by power cable with similar French water tidal plants across the English Channel in

order to form a grid of constant utility for both countries.

It has been estimated that the Severn project alone would
transform power equivalent to two billion kilowatt hours per
year, which would equal the saving of about a million tons
of coal annually. Now let us look at a twin project, such as
on the Rance River in France. This also would be a single-
basin project with a tidal variation between 38 and 11 feet
which should produce 700 million kilowatt hours annually.
Although the tidal variation at Mont St. Michel is greater,
42 to 12 feet, this project to be devolped would require a
dam over 14 miles long. If it ever should be built, it would
produce 25 billion kilowatt hours per year. This could be a
two-basin system, but at present it does not seem feasible
to attempt it in relation to the general setup of the French
electrical power system.

Coming to our own side of the Atlantic, the Bay of Fundy
in New Brunswick is well known to have some of the highest tides on earth, with a variation between 52 and 21 feet
between spring tides and the neap. Also, the geology of
the land structure is favorable, as the Petitcodiac and Memramcook estuaries converge into a bay and are separated
only by a narrow neck of rocky land which is ideal for a
two-basin system. Here, depending on the system used,
Canada could develop either 1.3 billion kilowatt hours of
variable energy per year or 0.3 billion kilowatt hours of
firm energy. The cost of this, according to estimates made in
the 1930's, would be as expensive as power from coal, cost-
ing about seven dollars a ton. At present rates this looks
rather high unless great need for industrial power should
develop in the New Brunswick area.

This brings us to the much-discussed Passamaquoddy project which was hailed either as a great step in industrial thinking or as a boondoggle, according to political viewpoint. Actually the first study of power from tides in this place was made by Dexter P. Cooper, the famous engineer, in the 1920's. He proposed an international two-basin project supported alike by Canada and the United States. The Canadian government finally withdrew from this cooperative idea because of a belief that it might hurt the important herring industry of this region. The American government then continued to make expensive surveys for an entirely American system augmented by a pumping station to insure a firm power output. Congress never approved this project and it died on the vine.

Aside from the political aspects, the Passamaquoddy project is no doubt quite feasible from an engineering standpoint and would develop under the two-basin system about 578 million kilowatt hours of firm power per year. But here again the practical considerations of cost of installation and the present remoteness from industrial areas makes it an uneconomical project. Another, single-basin, plan would also produce power but at too high an original cost.

So aside from a possible use of tidal power in southern England and northern France, either separately or in conjunction, the inevitable test that meets all our search for power prevails: Is the final output of energy high enough in proportion to the original investment and maintenance costs to make it possible in our present economy, and is there an industrial population near enough at hand to consume the production?

It is obvious from this brief survey that tidal power, like

so many other kinds of energy that seem readily available, is only a partial answer to the mounting needs of man under the present day industrial system. But there is one more source of great interest and some limited practicality that we might call God-given because of its natural origin from the sun, and this is the possible use of temperature differences between the surface and deep ocean waters in the tropics.

The property of water which enables the ocean surface to store heat without quick dispersal to the underlying layers accounts for a difference of 40 degrees between the surface and the deeps in hot latitudes. Man can take advantage of this natural and constant differential, and by certain devices these temperature extremes have been made to operate usefully turbo-electric generators. The basic energy comes from the sun's radiation trapped, as in a storage battery, by the salt sea. Although there is a loose comparison to the energy of the wind freed by the unequal heating of the atmosphere, there are certain very important differences in the thermal powers of the oceans and the airs.

The atmosphere, for instance, is heated from below as the sun's rays, falling upon the earth as light, are first absorbed and then liberated or re-radiated into the air as heat. In this way the lower part of the atmosphere becomes warmer. When it increases in warmth it becomes lighter than the upper air and rises. This change dissipates the heat energy in turbulent winds and in the end again radiates the energy back into space. This convection, combined with the great differences in air temperature at the poles and the Equator, creates the major wind systems of the earth.

The seas, on the contrary, receive their solar energy not

from below but from above so that the situation is reversed. Thus the sea becomes cooler as we go deeper. This makes the sea much more stable than the air and more resistant to vertical movements such as the often-violent convection storms which are characteristic over the land, notably in our thunder showers. The fact that the surface of the tropical sea is heated causes it to remain of lesser density than the deep waters and therefore resistant to sinking or mixing with them. But here another factor enters, namely the surface evaporation which in turn makes the surface of the sea saltier. The wind currents and the effect of the earth's rotation carry this water away from the Equator towards the polar regions where it cools off and, being saltier and therefore heavier, as it loses temperature it sinks. So in the subpolar regions there are great vertical currents which amount altogether to about four million tons per second in the North Atlantic alone. Unfortunately, these movements are too slow and unduly diffused to be harnessed as useful power in spite of their great volume. Nor have we ever arrived at a method of making use of the great horizontal oceanic currents such as the 75 million tons a second of the Gulf Stream, nor of the Kurio Shio, the Humboldt or the Brazilian currents. But we can make use of the vertical temperature difference in the tropics to drive turbines that provide electrical energy.

In the ordinary type of steam turbine with which we are familiar, the steam is generated in boilers where the pressures are higher than those of the atmosphere. This steam then passes to condensers in which the temperature is lowered by heat exchange. The drop of steam pressure from boiler to condenser moves the steam which on its way, just as a stream of water might, turns the wheels of the turbine. The final condensation of steam to water results in a further drop of pressure in the condenser and imparts a greater energy of motion to the drive of the steam through the turbine.

Operation of the recently devised sea-water turbines depends on the 40° difference between surface and bottom waters in tropical areas when put to use under much reduced pressures. The surface water at 80° F. is well below the boiling point of water under normal conditions. But we are used to thinking of water at the atmospheric pressure of 14 lbs to the square inch. We know that at this pressure water boils at 212° F. But, of course, at lower pressures water will boil at lower than the normal temperature just as it does in high mountain altitudes where boiling water is not hot enough to cook eggs. So, taking advantage of this, the warm surface water of the tropical sea can be made to boil and form steam by running it into a boiler under reduced pressure, and it is this type of boiler that is used for the sea-thermal engine. The condenser is also under vacuum and in it the steam is cooled and condensed by cold sea water pumped from 500 fathoms or more where the temperature averages around 40° F. This temperature difference of 40 degrees between the surface and the undersea proves sufficient to create the pressure differences needed to operate a turbine.

Although this sounds like a relatively simple operation there have been many practical engineering difficulties in building low-pressure turbines such as this. Only in recent years has any serious attempt been made to set up a turbo-electric plant for the utilization of this ever-present oceanic thermal energy. The original idea was proposed by Dr. G. Claude, and in 1926 and again in 1934 he made unsuccessful attempts to construct pilot plants. But since 1942 the French government has undertaken detailed studies of the problems involved and after six years of work, the Société Energie des Mers was established to build a full-scale power plant at Abidjan on the Ivory Coast of West Africa.

The plant now building at Abidjan will generate 7,000 kilowatts. Here are some of the engineering problems which faced its designers. Since the working steam pressure is low, the turbine wheel has necessarily to be of considerable size and it will actually measure 26 feet in diameter and operate at 600 r.p.m. This necessarily makes the plant of greater dimensions than other natural energy plants of similar power production. A more serious problem arose from the fact that there is air dissolved in sea water and when the water is boiled at low presures this dissolved air is immediately released. This would obviously upset the operation of the turbine, as, unlike steam, the air does not become liquefied when cooled again in the condenser. To overcome this handicap a rotary extractor designed by M. Rateau in 1929 has been used to remove the air from the water prior to its use and this device has proved satisfactory.

In the future other answers to these problems may be devised, for instance, in place of water, the use in the turbine of an intermediate liquid of lower boiling point, which could be boiled by the hot sea-water supply without applying reduced pressure. This would necessitate, however, the use of heat exchangers of a large capacity and these would incur further loss of energy.

Many practical difficulties have arisen, some of them as

apparently simple as the pumping of the cold water from the ocean deep. A great amount of this is required, over 10 tons per second. In order to reduce friction losses it was necessary to design a semi-rigid pipe 8 feet in diameter and long enough to reach from the power plant on shore across the inshore shallow waters until the steep fall-away to the ocean floor could be reached. This pipe also has to be sufficiently strong to withstand the currents of the sea and the pounding of the waves. In future plants some of these difficulties may be overcome by using a floating power plant permanently moored at sea where a pipe could be dropped vertically to the required depth. The power in this case could be transmitted to land by a submerged electric cable. Claude tried out such an experiment in the earlier stages of developing his sea-turbine but met with difficulties at that time which caused him to abandon the notion of a floating generator.

Limited industrial experiments have already been made at Bercy in France as a test of plant economy which confirmed the belief that the Abidjan plant in Africa could operate with only an eighth of its total power production used up by pumping and other auxiliary machinery. If this works out the plant should be able to function economically. The principal cost will be in the plant construction because its size is large in proportion to output of power. The initial cost of the generator, though high, should not be much different from that of a hydroelectric plant of the same production. But the initial cost is also offset by the special advantage of this type of operation, namely, there is no outlay for fuel. Here, energy is used one step nearer the main source of all our power, the direct radiation of the sun.

Dependence on thermal differences in the sea naturally limits the geographical use of an ocean thermal heat engine to tropical waters where there are cool depths of sea close to shore. Though a profoundly interesting advance in engineering technique is embodied in this thermal engine it is obviously limited and localized in its uses by the existence of satisfactory conditions such as in the Pacific or the West Indies where a comparatively small plant near the seashore would serve already established centers of population.

Even though plants such as that now building at Abidijan can never solve our major problems of world-wide energy consumption, they may well answer important local needs in places such as we have mentioned, particularly when our fossil fuels become more scarce and expensive. In addition, the use of heat exchangers instead of the cold water injection condensers of the Abidjan plant would also make possible the preparation of drinking water and of salt extraction, without additional expenditures of energy.

Before we leave the subject of salt-water power, if we take another look at the table of energy requirements in the previous chapter, it is evident that neither tidal power nor ocean thermal plants can supply more than a negligible part of what is called for in the future. Here again our attention is once more driven back to direct solar heat and to plant growth in the sea and on the land for a permanently renewable source of energy that can answer more than purely local needs. It is true that the Severn Dam and the Abidjan deep-water turbine can well be put to use in their particular localities, but we are concerned with a future world energy requirement that calls for a more universal application irrespective of tidal reservoirs and special temperature differentials. But before we have finished with the ocean, we must turn to another kind of shortage which mankind will eventually face, the solution for which may lie in the dilute and vast resources of elements and minerals which are held in the oceanic reservoir.

# CHAPTER 9

# Mining the Seas

IN COURSE OF OUR STOCKTAKING OF the sources of power needed by mankind for food, industry and heating our homes, it has become pretty clear that we are truly pensioners of the continuous and renewable energy of the sun in the quantities needed merely to keep pace with the pressing demands of the world population. Being creatures of the earth we have been dependent on what the land can bring forth, and this, we find, has definite inescapable limitations. So we turn to the abundant seas and explore new possibilities, limited but continuous, for trapping the power of the sun in forms available to us for useful purposes.

But we are the prisoners as well as the masters of our environment. The power of which we speak, whether of life or of factories, can only operate through matter. So we have also to consider the solid substance of living organisms and the materials which make up the framework of our machines and the food and fuels in which energy has already been stored by virtue of chemical changes. How long can these material resources last, this capital wealth, which we now use with ever-increasing skills and in rapidly mounting quantity? And how much may we expect in new mineral wealth from the ocean?

It is only in the last minute of time that man has been forced to consider the fundamental difference between the sources of energy and of the material wealth of land and sea. The energy of the sun is certainly as eternal as man's brief tenure of the earth. It is continuously reaching the outer envelope of our atmosphere. Some of it is absorbed by the ground and undergoes many transformations which we have, in part, discussed. But eventually all of this energy of sunlight, whether it reaches the ground or not, also leaves the earth as heat radiation to be dissipated back into the infinity of space. Our material substances, such as minerals, follow a different pattern of distribution. The earth neither continuously receives them nor to any significant extent loses them. For most purposes we can consider the materials of the earth as indestructible. But this does not mean that they are always available just when and where we need them or in the forms or concentrations in which we can best use them. This is obvious in some minerals which are widely scattered and present almost everywhere on earth, but which are found either in the wrong form or too thinly concentrated to be of use to us. Aluminum, for instance, is present in quantity in the clay soil of most of our gardens and farms but in a form difficult to extract. This is true of many common minerals. Others, like uranium, are also generally distributed but in such minute quantities that we can only extract them at prodigious and wasteful cost and effort. Our real job is to find the substances we need in a concentrated form readily useful for our industrial civilization.

Iron, of course, in the form of ores, is widely distributed

in small quantities but thanks to ancient geological processes it is also concentrated in a few rich pockets. We have learned to mine these concentrations and to refine them still further into the pure metal. But we can't do this without expending energy in the chemical process of reduction in our smelters and blast furnaces. Here we draw on capital resources of coal and the ratio of coal per ton of ore increases with the smelting of poorer qualities of the iron ore.

What happens in this transformation of our metallic mineral wealth? We take the concentrations of nature and continue to concentrate them further in buildings, ships or machinery. The final form of the pure metal or alloy is usually more unstable than the original ores. Iron and steel change back into the oxides as rust and are dissipated into our city dumps and auto-graveyards where the process goes on into thinner and thinner concentrations so that at long last, as dust or through rain and drainage-canals and the rivers, they are carried away into the sea. We draw upon the bank account of the earth's accidental bounty, use this for a second of time compared to its slow geological accumulation, and then it slips from us into the dilute reservoir of the oceans.

Only in the case of a few minerals is there ever a return path from ocean to land and this can be of no consequence to us, because the geological upheavals which bring this about, when eventually repeated many millions of years hence, could well wipe man from the face of the earth. It happens this way. Directly, or through the agency of life in the seas, the minerals are deposited on the sea floor as sedimentary rock. If this occurs in deep waters they are probably lost for good to the surface of the earth. If the deposits are in shallow waters fringing the continents, it is possible that one of the great cataclysms of nature, which occur in cycles of hundreds of millions of years, may eventually lift the sea floors high and dry and restore their minerals to land. But this is academic as far as the race of men is concerned.

Although iron and most other metals follow this one-way path of dissipation in form, there are other materials necessary to us which follow cycles whereby they remain in a continuous supply, replenished as fast as they are used. Water as the most common and basic necessity of life follows such a cycle. When water accumulates on the land it drains by river and stream into the salt sea. We have already discussed how the sun raises it again from the oceans by evaporation and so by rainfall completes the cycle back to land and balances the budget. Only when man interferes with this natural turn of the wheel is there an interruption of this permanent supply. It varies, of course, from place to place and time to time, but the total supply of rain to land is reasonably steady and continuous.

Another basic element necesary to all living things is nitrogen and this is also cyclical in distribution. The air is its great reservoir where it composes four-fifths of our atmosphere. From there it is continuously removed by leguminous plants, by certain types of bacteria and by the action of lightning, and thus fertilizes both the land and the sea. Transposed by the decay of plant and animal life, through the agency of bacterial and chemical change, elementary nitrogen gas returns to the air, so that the concentrations in the land, the sea and the air tend to remain balanced so long as other conditions are unchanged. An equilibrium between nitrogen in the air and that dissolved in salt and fresh waters completes this balance.

Perhaps the element most closely linked to life, however, is carbon. There is in this case, too, a cyclical balance between the carbon dioxide in the air and in solution in the sea and that part of it which is combined in the organic compounds of living plants and animals. The amount of carbon dioxide daily absorbed by vegetation and built into sugars, starches and other carbohydrates is fairly evenly balanced by the amount breathed out by animals and plants during the chemical process of turning the energy of food into that of life. Also, as with nitrogen, the amount of carbon dioxide in the air is balanced against that dissolved in fresh water and the waters of the sea. It is true that coal and oil represent a withdrawal of carbon from this cycle, but this is temporary and insufficient to materially alter the supply in the air.

Carbon compounds are vital to us, since they store in plant life the energy trapped from the sun by photosynthesis. Plants on land and in the sea hold ready a permanent supply of carbon in an almost perfect cycle of renewable availability to man as it is released by the consumption of vegetation for food or fuel. Only where carbon is trapped, unused, in fossil fuels is there a one-way track and this is too slight to matter.

As far as our term on earth goes mankind can think of his resources as more or less either cyclical or noncyclical. Some of the relatively noncyclical resources appear to us as a permanent part of the land as, for instance, limestone rock. The category into which we can put them depends on what time schedule we use. For ordinary consideration, limestone dissolves or leaches into our rivers and follows a one-way path to the sea. But geologically considered in a timing of millions of years, this lime, carried down by sea life or directly deposited on the sea floor of shallow seas, may, as we have seen, form rock again. When heaved up during the wide-spaced periods of geological change, this rock may again be returned to land areas. The cliffs of Dover and the Dolomite Mountains were thus at one time beneath the seas. But where the deposits are in the great deeps, they are lost. The balance here is acyclical and, slowly over ages great beyond our own concern, there has been a tendency for this deposit of lime rock in the sea to increase in deeper waters. The slow loss of lime to the sea will, millions of years from now, cause the land to become more acid and the sea more alkaline.

Of more pressing concern is the rapid dissipation of our nonrenewable coal and oil reserves. In answer to this we have pointed out the possibilities of new uses of vegetation on land and particularly in the sea as a steady source of sun energy. Butt here is a much more serious threat to the human race in the loss of our phosphorus sources. As phosphates, this mineral is continually dissolving from the rocks and from our soils and washing away into the sea at the rate of 20 million tons every year. This amount is lost to the land except for two rather minor cycles of return.

Again, one of these cycles of renewal is geologically too remote to be of use to us, namely the upheaval of sedimentary phosphatic rock such as we now mine from lands that were once the floor of the shallow seas. A more immediate and useful cycle is illustrated by the sea birds which, off the coasts of Peru, drop their dung on rocky islands in the form of guano. This constant redepositing of phosphorus accounts for a net return to land of only about 10,000 tons a year. Phosphorus, then, must be considered in its general utility to man as belonging to a dangerously rapid acyclical process of transference from land to sea.

It is fortunate that such basic materials as carbon, nitrogen and water have a continuous cycle of redistribution, but, whether cyclic or noncyclic, the major part of our metals and minerals are either only partly cyclic or are completely noncyclic, traveling a path of little or no return. These natural courses are further complicated by man's interference. This is obvious enough in the exploitation of the one-way materials or our nonrenewable resources which disappear with increasing rapidity as we increase our use of them. In the case of the balanced cyclic processes of material distribution, the effect of man's interference is harder to predict because the natural balance may, up to a point, be re-established. But there is a critical point beyond which a greater level of exploitation might bring about rapid and adverse effects.

In the case of phosphorus we have seen that the cycle of distribution is only partially in balance so that, when it is removed from the land by agricultural processes or man-made erosion, the results are direct and fairly easy to predict. We mine phosphate rock each year to the extent of about two million tons of elementary phosphorus and this is mostly used on the land. One way or another the greater part of this eventually reaches the sea. The only small return to land comes where plankton lives on phosphorus fertilizer, fishes feed on the plankton and man or the seabirds capture and use a fraction of these fish. Statistically it can be shown that not more than sixty or seventy thousand tons of phosphorus are thus annually returned to land, and this amounts to less than 4 per cent of the total annual loss to the sea. Here, then, is a vital depletion which, though its end is far in the future, will eventually impose on man the necessity of devising methods to complete the cycle and to recapture our phosphorus from the oceans. Failing this, our vegetable crops, which need this fertilizing agent, will be reduced and famine come upon us.

But there is one effect of man's interference with natural cyclical distribution that is right under our noses and this is the exploitation of fresh-water supplies. The fresh-water table, so necessary to our prosperity, is radically affected today by what we call the conquest of the land. It is being depleted by soil erosion, the mishandling of pasture and forest lands, and the general destruction of adequate ground cover. In a virgin state the organic materials of the topsoil provide a natural absorbent layer which soaks up and retains the rains. When, through deforestation, overgrazing, excessive use of chemical fertilizers, and other causes this layer is destroyed, the rapid runoff of rain causes soil erosion and resultant flash floods speed up the normal seepage of water from land to sea. Thus our ground water reserves, necessary not only to agriculture but to industry, are not absorbed. We not only lose the use of the abundant water cycle but its swift flooding to the sea carries away annually immense quantities of irreplaceable fertile soil.

This interference of man with nature in building his modern mechanized civilization is now forcing us suddenly to come awake to the very real dangers of blind progress and make a close inventory of the materials and minerals of the earth's bounty. We must inspect our storeroom, and see where the cupboard is bare. This will point up and measure the urgency with which we must tackle the problem of learning to mine the salt storehouse of the sea and to extract metals and industrial raw materials from the dilute solution of our oceanic wealth. In doing this we must always bear in mind that mechanical techniques are also dependent on the concentration and the availability of the ores in relation to our industrial centers. Looking at the present land resources of the United States in this light, together with the phenomenal increase of industrial demands during the past half-century, we find an approaching dearth of many metals and a serious deficiency in others. Today, practically all the high-grade iron ore has been used up and we have commenced importing from Venezuela. We have also commenced to smelt low-grade ores which would have been ignored twenty-five years ago. This handicap is, of course, compounded by the fact that the amounts of fuel and power needed to work poorer and poorer ore increase out of all proportion to the intrinsic value. Poorer ore means an increase in coal consumption per ton and thus the nonrenewable energy sources are being taxed to rapid exhaustion. Any reliance upon our nonrenewable resources forces us into a complicated network of interlocking problems related to the sources and uses of energy.

And while we are at it, the nature of man being what it is, we must consider not only our peacetime industrial vulnerability, but also where the United States stands in case of war in relation to basic resources. Copper, which is so universally used in our economy, will probably be gone forever within one more generation. What if we cannot reach the copper that exists elsewhere on the globe? A similar situation can arise in the case of aluminum which has suddenly become of such importance that it is now virtually indispensable to our industrial world. Today, the greater part of our bauxite, the basic aluminum ore, is brought to us in great fleets from other parts of the world. General Marshall pointed this up in a letter to Admiral King in 1942:

> ". . . 22 percent of the bauxite fleet has already been destroyed; 20 percent of the Puerto Rico fleet has been lost; tanker sinkings have been 3.5 percent per month of tonnage now in use."

The zinc and lead produced in the United States today do not begin to supply our current needs. Other metals needed in smaller but essential quantities for our alloys also have to be imported. All of our tin comes from abroad and nickel and manganese needed for our alloy steels are insufficient here for our peacetime needs. Soviet Russia, it can be said, is well endowed with most of these essential minerals, except copper and aluminum, either within its own borders or in the satellite countries it controls. Other minerals it lacks are to be found close to its borders. The adjoining chart of world mineral resources well illustrates the picture.

The United States Department of the Interior, certainly not an alarmist source of information, pointed out in 1945 that the situation is not simply a question of anticipating future scarcities. It flatly stated "we are relatively weak now." In 1947 the Department estimated that mercury ores are 97 per cent gone, silver and lead, 83 per cent gone, vanadium, 78 per cent, zinc and copper and oil, 60 per cent gone, and

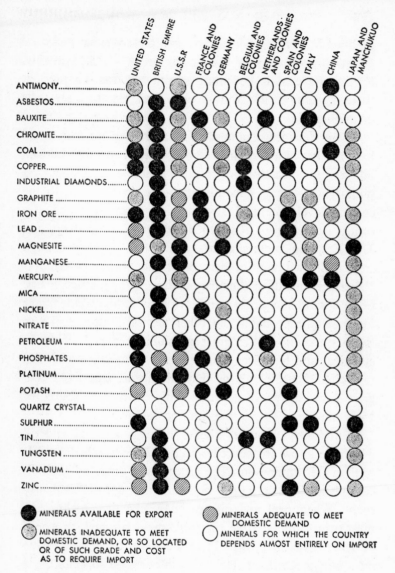

*Figure 21*. Mineral Resources: Self-sufficiency of Selected Countries in Major Minerals.

high-grade iron deposits almost completely exhausted with about three-fourths of the low-grade ores still available. High-grade coal is becoming scarce but, for the present, there is plenty of lower grade coal available at higher costs of mining.

These statistics of approaching scarcities are mentioned here not because they are new to us. They are well known, but we use them to point to our inevitable dependence on photosynthesis and minerals of the sea rather than to the endless development of new chemical processes alone. Recently, in their book *Road to Abundance*, Jacob Rosin and Max Eastman quote similar statistics but, properly enough from their own point of view, draw attention to the remarkable achievements of chemistry in developing plastics, fibers, fabrics, synthetic rubber and nylon as modern substitutes for vegetable products and other natural materials. There is no question of the great possibilities ahead of us in chemical and technical developments of new materials for replacing our minerals as they disappear. But there is a grave lack, so far, of a permanently continuous source of basic material. This is the limiting factor.

A majority of our synthetics come from coal and oil which we know are nonrenewable and for which the sands of time are running out. The processes of time and geological upheaval set up a once-rich bank account that is nearly spent. When coal and oil are gone, chemical technology must turn to replaceable vegetable materials such as wood, or search for an answer in artificial photosynthesis. This must be done without stealing from our food supplies. And they will still need energy for their manufacture. The roseate test-tube world of the modern chemist is still a dependent one. And this dependency leads directly and inescapably in the near future to the need of trapping more energy from the sun and the harvesting of more vegetation from the sea.

In view of the existing scarcity of many materials and the impending scarcity of others, we must consider what chance we have of finding adequate substitutes for them. Certainly the quest for new energy sources will help because power is increasingly needed to work the poorer grades of ore. But, as we have seen, nearly all of our material resources end up in the sea. The problem of collecting diffuse materials from the sea and that of mining poorer and more scattered ores on land are somewhat analogous, but it is obviously much easier to pump great quantities of water than to laboriously dig and transport and pulverize and dissolve dilute ores. Differences in concentration are compensated for by the ease of handling water.

When we talk of mining the sea we must think of it as a great reservoir constantly being charged with materials we need. Salt is the basic content. It is probable that the oceans have always been salt, although not as salty as they now are. The chemical composition suggests that the water may actually have been derived in the beginning from the primary rocks of the earth. Whatever view we take of its origin, the fact remains that 7,000 cubic miles of fresh water from rivers enter the sea each year. This water brings with it further supplies of minerals, including an estimated 160,000,000 tons of common salt alone. Since about an equal amount of sea water evaporates from the sea, it necessarily is becoming saltier, although very, very slowly.

Various kinds of deposits are continuously being added

to the ocean floor. Muds and clays which contain silica, aluminum and copper are deposited by rivers close to their mouths. Besides these, there are chemical deposits which form blue muds containing iron in the fairly deep water, and red silica clays, from volcanic material, collect in the deepest waters. There is also found in deep water a fairly pure silica deposited from the raining down of skeletons of dead microscopic organisms of plankton known as radiolarians. Some parts of the ocean floor are mainly a diatomaceous ooze, also siliceous, formed from the skeletons of planktonic diatoms. In the shallow waters limestone muds are found in increasing quantities. They are made up of foraminifera, but where the waters are warm the lime deposits come from small molluscs called pteropods. Shallow tropical waters deposit limestone from corals and related growths.

Lime, iron and other kinds of material deposited on the sea floors are obviously no part of a cyclic distribution that can be useful to man in his stabilized environment. There are other minerals lost thus to the floor of the ocean reservoir. The decomposition of marine organisms deposits nodules of phosphate which contain as much as 50 per cent calcium phosphate in some parts of the sea. Manganese, likewise, is deposited. The submarine mineral, glauconite, is a potassium iron silicate. These are all well out of reach, and if we intend to mine the seas, we have to turn to the minerals which are dissolved in sea water and to forget those on the ocean bottom.

Here we have a mass of 300 million cubic miles of water holding great wealth in solution. We can get some inventory of this by considering the contents dissolved in a single cubic mile. On the average there are about 166 million tons of salts in this cubic mile of water. In the appended table, the first five or six metals show what great quantities of minerals are suspended in the sea water. But aside from the common salt, sodium chloride, they still exist in dilute quantity compared to the vast extent of the medium. It has been possible, nevertheless, to mine some of them from the ocean, namely salt, magnesium and bromine. Even though uranium exists in the sea to the extent of one or two billion tons, it still must be considered a trace element as far as its availability is concerned. There

## TABLE III

### APPROXIMATE AMOUNT OF MINERALS IN ONE CUBIC MILE OF SEA WATER

| | |
|---|---|
| Sodium Chloride (common salt) | 120,000,000 tons |
| Magnesium Chloride | 18,000,000 tons |
| Magnesium Sulphate | 8,000,000 tons |
| Calcium Sulphate | 6,000,000 tons |
| Potassium Sulphate | 4,000,000 tons |
| Calcium Carbonate (lime) | 550,000 tons |
| Magnesium Bromide | 350,000 tons |
| Bromine | 300,000 tons |
| Strontium | 60,000 tons |
| Boron | 21,000 tons |
| Fluorine | 6,400 tons |
| Barium | 900 tons |
| Iodine | 100 to 12,000 tons |
| Arsenic | 50 to 350 tons |
| Rubidium | 200 tons |
| Silver | up to 45 tons |
| Copper, Manganese, Zinc, Lead | 10 to 30 tons |
| Gold | up to 25 tons |
| Radium | about ⅙ ounce |
| Uranium | 7 tons |

are many millions of millions of tons of bromine in sea water but we are not able to extract more than two ounces from a single ton.

Table salt, of course, is in quite a different category. This has been recovered from the sea since the early days of mankind. It has been evaporated in salt ponds in warm countries by the Greeks, Romans and, even earlier, by the Chinese more than two thousand years before Christ. The United States produces today about 350,000 tons a year, and the world production is four or five million tons annually. After the salt has been removed from the sea water by solar evaporation, the remaining liquid, called bittern, contains such valuable minerals as potassium chloride, magnesium chloride, magnesium sulphate, and calcium and sodium sulphate. Although these minerals are mined from present land deposits, some are obtained by evaporation from the sea and, if necessary, this quantity could be extended without limit.

We mentioned that bromine had been successfully mined from the sea. Here is an example of good returns in spite of a great dilution, for it exists in quantities of less than a pound to a ton of sea water. As early as 1926, attempts were made to extract bromine from the bitterns left from solar salt processes but the greater part still came from mineral brine pumped from mines. However, the rapid increase in demand for bromine to make gasoline anti-knock compounds created a scarcity, and in 1933 the Dow Chemical Company turned to the sea and erected a plant to extract the element from unconcentrated sea water without evaporation. By 1938 this plant had a yearly production of 20,000 tons.

The same company has also pioneered in the extraction

of magnesium from the ocean. During the war a plant was built which reached an output of 40,000 tons a year. Although the war demand is now gone, new uses for magnesium and its alloys are being discovered all the time. This pioneering effort has resulted in economic success. Mining the ocean has been made to pay. Today the entire production of magnesium in the United States is from the sea, and about 80 per cent of today's bromine is derived from sea water. In addition to this, two companies in Great Britain also extract magnesium from the ocean.

Other minerals in our cubic mile of sea water, such as potassium and iodine, may be extracted more cheaply today from terrestrial salt deposits such as those found at Stassfurt and in Chile. These deposits were once undersea sediments laid down in closed-off branches of ancient seas where isolation and evaporation, alternating with new supplies of salt water, acted as a kind of huge pumping and drying system. But these deposits now on land are nonrenewable in any cycle useful to man and one day we shall have to turn directly to the sea for them.

The table of quantity of minerals in the sea is impressive but unfortunately no more so than the measure of their dilution. It is this lack of concentration that makes it very doubtful, even with all our skills, that all of them will ever be useful to us in economic quantity. The process for their extraction, however, exists and has been observed where most efficient, in the cell tissues of marine plants and animals. Here, by continuous and living operations the seaweeds, for instance, can extract iodine salts from the sea, which scarcely appear even as a trace in chemical analysis of the water. The weeds concentrate this so that man can obtain iodine from treating them. When we can learn this direct trick of extraction from the water, we will be nearer economic success in mining the oceans for other trace metals as well as iodine. Small soft-bodied sea squirts, or tunicates, are even able to extract the metal vanadium from the salt water, and yet it is almost impossible for our chemists to find this trace by laboratory analysis until the sea squirt has done his job. Other shellfish and seaweeds concentrate in a similar manner from the thin sea solution copper, cobalt, silica and other important minerals.

A present inventory of utility for our mine of the sea comes down to the concentrated forms of common salt, magnesium, and bromine as the economically valuable minerals now available to us. What, then, are the chances for man to extract beneficially useful quantities of the many more dilute minerals in the sea? Frankly, what we can do in the laboratory is still a long way from successful translation into commercial operation. But here again the lack of attention to these problems, more than the want of basic method, is the trouble. With more research and technological development we may well one day successfully pump the mineral wealth from the millions of cubic miles of the ocean mines.

Some recently developed processes offer hope in this direction. Ion-exchange resins, for instance, have come out of the laboratory stage into commercial use in recent years, and by using them we may be able to by-pass the customary evaporation process which is costly in power. At present we have to separate the mineral salts from large quantities of sea water and then separate the salts from each other. The direct method of sun evaporation is not so expensive, but it is only available where the shoreline and optimum conditions of sunlight and nearby markets make it feasible. Exchange resins operate without the need for fuel and heat to evaporate the water and with a lesser expenditure for regeneration. Here the mineral is removed from the water, at a great saving of power, rather than the water from the mineral.

Other laboratory methods which may come to commercial fruition are based on the gradual, selective removal of minerals at different rates and at different points of an absorbing column. This is called chromatographic absorption, and might conceivably be applied to mineral extraction from sea water if given sufficient study and development.

And, of course, man can take a lesson from his own efficient machinery such as the osmotic separation of useful food from the watery content of his own intestines. It is possible to manufacture artificial membranes through which water will pass while the dissolved mineral salts are caught and concentrated. Practically, it is difficult to construct a sufficiently strong semi-permeable membrane, but there are claims that this has been accomplished by indirect means and a patent applied for. We can see from an inventory of the pathfinders now at work that the frontier for a true scientific advance along trails already laid down certainly awaits us in the future. Research and engineering development will tell us when.

Now let us get back to the most plentiful of all salt-water minerals, the 300 million cubic miles of the water itself. Here the problem is to avoid the expensive use of fuels to evaporate the water from the salts it contains. This has already been avoided by the use of low temperature evaporation at greatly reduced pressure, but it is still too costly except for restricted domestic uses. The answer to this problem may lie, perhaps, in the low pressure thermal turbines, such as those at Abidjan, which we described in the previous chapter. In a world of increasing fuel shortages, this method has the great advantage that power is produced rather than absorbed. It is only one step removed from a sun engine using the energy of direct radiation. The efficiency of this thermal turbine sea-water system might well be increased by covering the source of hot water, the salt coastal lagoons, with oil layers which would absorb greater heat from the sun than the sea itself. This process is of obvious value in isolated places such as islands and desert sea-coasts, and its commercial success might be further improved if it is used in combination with mineral extraction. Many of the methods for extracting minerals can also be used for extracting fresh water from sea water. This is true of the osmotic semi-permeable membrane and for the ion-exchange process. In fact, this last method has been used successfully in sea-survival safety kits which makes it a particular candidate for large-scale commercial development.

We have mentioned the many new materials that modern chemistry has been producing from the basic fossil fuels such as coal and oil. One of the great advantages of a balanced use of our world resource bank would be to take the pressure off these nonrenewable accounts of coal and oil by substituting the organic vegetable wealth of the sea. New sources of sea energy or direct solar energy would release our organic fuels for chemical manufacture rather than for wasteful spending in heat and power. Chemistry has already developed a fantastic range of fabrics, medical drugs, structural materials and plastics, as well as our new synthetic antibiotics. But this is a drain on many resources that are either nonrenewable or difficult of extension. A great new impulse to chemical development will open up with the first successful expanding of renewable energy sources or of large-scale harvesting of the sea's plankton.

It is plain that there is no single magic answer to the problem of supply and demand, of the put and take of energy, that runs our industrial civilization. It boils down to this. There are shortages developing rapidly in our concentrated land ores. Against this there are vast but dilute resources still untapped in the sea. The dilute land resources will in turn become available to us, but at a high price in expended energy. The oceanic resources are easier to handle even though dilute. And the sea is an inexhaustible mine with a continual augmentation from land drainage.

In the future the ocean must take its place as a source of mineral wealth equal at least to the role played by the rocks of the land. Likewise, we are now alert to the role the ocean pastures can play as a source of vegetable energy which can relieve the present growing pressure on coal and oil as power, and leave them free for purposes of chemical manufacture. How soon this can come about depends on how seriously man pushes both research and technological development of latent ocean resource. This is the present bottleneck.

# CHAPTER 10

# No Eldorado

So far in this book we have tried to make an inventory of the present and future resources which can help to stabilize our immediate needs and guarantee a healthy future for our world. This path has led to the sea, which remains the last great reservoir of food and minerals and energy not yet subject to the will of man. In good times it is hard for us to grasp the simple fact that we no longer live within an expanding frontier of free land and limitless resources. Surrounded by the abundance of an American supermarket, the fact that half the peoples of the world live under constant threat of starvation seems quite unreal. Yet we do feel on our necks the chaos and uncertainty of world conditions: Europe straining for a minimum prosperity, Asiatic peoples in revolt, and the comfortable arrangements of colonialism everywhere challenged. Basically, this all springs from a count of full and empty dinner pails. All over the world, crowded societies of half-starved peoples no longer accept their economic inequality as fate. They are assuming the birthright of an equal share of the world's goods, at least as far as subsistence goes, but is there enough to share?

In the last thirty years of the nineteenth century, 20 million people died in India from starvation. There is still an uncontrolled population growth throughout Asia. In the ten years between 1931 and 1941 India's population increased by 50 million. It is estimated that China will probably grow at the rate of 40 to 60 million every ten years. Our own population has dropped its tendency to level off and is on the increase again. It is necessary to ask if it seems reasonable that in the next few decades the world can create new food and energy resources to give a decent chance of life to the millions of new souls crowding onto this planet. Between 1650 and 1950 the world population more than quadrupled. The western frontiers absorbed the shock. These frontiers are gone today. In another ten years the world food supply will have to be increased by at least 25 per cent in order merely to maintain our present totally inadequate ratio of supply.

Is there any hope that we will make a concerted worldwide attempt to curb this spate of population? Practically none. In the West little will be done because of theological-political reasons and for want of sensing the problem. In Asia, although the problem is realized in spots, the solution is decades away. India has officially started a campaign to limit her population through birth-control. But there is no need here to go into this question—important as it may be—because we are dealing with a present situation of supply and demand, with the resource-population ratio, and the flooding march of mankind is upon us willy-nilly. It is enough here to state the scientific point of view as expressed by Julian Huxley in his essays on evolution. Speaking of those who propose unlimited human breeding throughout the world he writes: "They are wrong because population increase is, together with war, the greatest present threat to civilization and progress; because, in so far as they are implemented in practice, they mean frustration and misery and ill-health and ignorance, not for millions but for thousands of millions of human souls; and because they would result in general failure to realize higher possibilities for mankind as a whole. But to me they are also wrong because they assert absolutely and dogmatically, instead of being conclusions arrived at by free inquiry as to what is best to do in particular circumstances."

Let's recapitulate these particular circumstances we have sketched in the preceding chapters. Our fossil fuels are on the way out. This is being hastened by the fact that our advances in chemistry are also drawing upon the same source, not only for power but to manufacture new kinds of goods. At present 92 per cent of our power demands are made on coal and oil. Other possible sources of expanded power such as hydroelectric developments, the wind, the tides and thermal sea-water turbines, we have seen, can be of little real assistance. What then of atomic power as a substitute source of energy for our machine age?

Here indeed is a great hope. It is safe to say that within the next ten years atomic power may be able to compete with coal in the production of electric energy. Indeed, if we can master the breeder reaction for commercial use, atomic energy reserves may be twenty-five times greater than coal. Here is a replacement for fossil fuels. But the catch is in its restricted uses and in the cost. Our present advantage comes from over two billion dollars spent in governmental research. There is also the problem of what to do with atomic waste which is radioactive and dangerous to mankind. And there is the ever-present factor of capital outlay, which at present is obviously excessive. Finally, on a long term basis, we can not escape the fact that our radioactive minerals are nonrenewable. Here at a later date we shall face the same dead-end that faces us now with fossil fuels.

But the sun and mankind are coexistent and the frontiers of usefulness for the sun's inexhaustible energy remain as a challenge and a hope. We have looked at the various methods now being studied for land uses of the sun's energy and have found that they have limitations of a geographic and economic nature. We have also looked to the sea and found that this path leads to greater resource, provided we can develop the research and the techniques to meet the opportunities.

We have been speaking in terms of power. What of that other constant demand of harvesting the food for the multitudes of the earth? There we have seen the finite limits of the land acres, combined with the problem of constant loss of land fertilizers. There also exists the dual demand on vegetable acreage, with industry and power as a rival to food production. But once more the pastures of Leviathan offer a way out with their limitless acreage of living plankton, constant and swiftly renewable under the rays of the sun. If we will meet the need in effort and intelligence science may lead us to an ocean of plenty.

We can also mine the deep, as we have pointed out in taking stock of the mineral wealth of the oceans. This is a wealth not mined to exhaustion but, on the contrary, constantly being replenished from the losses of the land.

The final answer to all these problems remains, of course,

within man himself. We stand at the end of a phase of happy and energetic exploitation. We have aimed not only for a bare subsistence but for a higher standard of living. What is this optimum existence for mankind? It can no longer carelessly be measured by the mere speed and variety of ways in which we consume the bounties of the earth and sea. It must rather be measured by the harmonious and intelligent development, within the range of what has been given us, of the fraction of the sun's energy that guarantees our continued survival in the enjoyment of peace and plenty on earth. In merely conquering nature, too often we unwillingly set the stage for our future extermination. The booming western frontier is finished. We must turn our minds to fresh frontiers. Since 1946 we have used up one and a half times the total amount of petroleum the world had previously consumed since its earliest production.

The questions raised here must also be answered by a stock-taking of ideas, as well as by an inventory of energy and material resource. Inasmuch as most of the answers at first glance fall into the realm of scientific research it is encouraging to note that the modern scientist no longer dares to regard himself as a monastic in pursuit of pure knowledge with no obligation to the society he lives in. The social and political implications of the atom bomb are a good enough example of how science has been made conscientiously and uncomfortably aware of its responsibilities in a mechanized age. Our society must recognize this increase in awareness of the pure scientist and we must find more ways and means of incorporating his knowledge and his experience into our national leadership. It is not enough that the research be used as an adjunct to profitable business or for the edification of learned societies. Democracy itself depends on the same open spirit of inquiry, the same leaping-over of national and religious lines, the same unbiased analysis of situations-in-being; that is the essence of a good scientific training.

This new attitude of science in relation to society emphasizes the nature of the problem we face. It is not simply a matter of laboratory experiment by magicians, by an impersonal "they" who will find some way out, somehow. It is not a matter of leaving it to business leaders who hope to guarantee a present prosperity. It is also not a matter for theological dogma in the political arena. It is a matter of common council among all elements of our society to decide where the path of our future well-being, if not our very existence, shall lead. As a people, beyond nation or profession or trade advantage, we must govern the haphazard consumption of nonrenewable resource. We must finance and extend, as a people, the discovery of new sources of energy, material wealth, and food supply. As regards the wealth of the sea, which may be the answer to the pressure of hungry populations, the question of international exploitation and common advantage is paramount, for the open seas have traditionally been realms of common usage. If these answers do not come from the private initiative of society, then answers may well have to be found, whether we like it or not, in socialized research and development. This is obvious enough in the exploration of new fishing grounds and the marketing, at decent prices, of potentially great new supplies from the sea.

Eventually the question of how far we can leave the dangerous and unstable pressure of random population increase to chance will have to be faced the world over. Here again are theological, economic and social considerations that cannot be solved in a test-tube world alone. At present we are manfully striving to breed food and energy fast enough to catch a runaway birthrate, and the prospects for catching up are not bright. Journalists and enthusiasts of various kinds try to say this isn't so. They point to *Chlorella*, to superphosphates, to the vast new purchasing power of more and more people on earth. But food and power from costly and nonrenewable sources, we have seen, will not give an answer, nor will a faster and faster consumption of our resources in expanding trade in mechanized gadgetry do anything but hasten the showdown. The equation of supply and use remains. Vegetation used for food in limited acreage leaves so much less for fuel and materials. Oil and coal used for plastics, medicines and building materials have to be deducted from their use for power. Already in the Argentine, the land of beef, the government is giving away free fish to the population because of meat shortages.

In reviewing the world cupboard we have made distinctions between food, energy and mineral or material requirements. We think there can be no argument that essential mineral wealth is in short supply and fast disappearing from the land. The dilute 300 million cubic miles of ocean is an untapped frontier of infinite supply. Energy that we need is fast going with our fossil fuels although on land it may get a far longer, though still temporary, lease of life from atomic energy developments. Our eternal source of energy

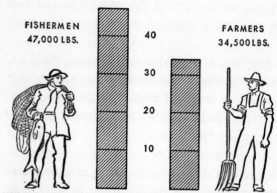

FISHERMEN
47,000 LBS.

40

30

20

10

FARMERS
34,500 LBS.

AVERAGE ANNUAL CONTRIBUTION OF EACH FISHERMAN AND FARMER TO TOTAL PRODUCTION

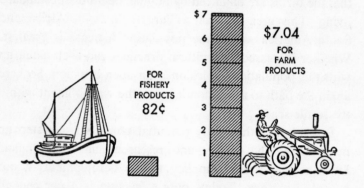

$7

6

5

4

3

2

1

FOR
FISHERY
PRODUCTS
82¢

$7.04
FOR
FARM
PRODUCTS

ANNUAL FEDERAL EXPENDITURES FOR EACH TON OF FOOD PRODUCED

*Figure 22.* Comparison between yield of land and sea in the U.S.A. Federal expenditures are very much smaller in proportion to the fishery yield than agricultural expenditures.

still remains the sun, mainly through the agency of photosynthesis. And here again the path to plenty leads to the millions of fertile acres of plankton in the seas, which not only serve purpose as sources of future energy but also present a vast renewable expanse of high protein food potential.

Medical geographers of the American Geographical Society report that only about one-third of the human race has an adequate diet in terms of protein, vitamin and mineral consumption and that the other two-thirds is deficient in caloric intake, protective foods, or both. This does not mean that all of this two-thirds of the world is starving to death. It does mean that they are in ill-health and inefficient as human beings compared to the fortunate minority and that the births are balanced by famine, death or substandard living. This area of want is largely in Asia, Africa and South America, where the population increase is greatest. Whether increased agricultural practices can even catch up with this population explosion is an open question. So here again the path to a solution leads to the wealth latent within the fertile seas.

But this wealth is only potential unless we can step up many times the money and research and technological know-how at present applied to the development of our oceanic resources. Today, only a fraction of 1 per cent of what is spent on land in solving agricultural problems is devoted to research in our great oceanic frontier.

What, then, is needed for developing the pastures of Leviathan? Certainly much purely scientific research into the life habits of fishes and the nature of their changing environment. Also, as companion to this, we require further and much enlarged experiment in methods of finding and catching fishes and marketing the catch at a price that consumers can pay. And beyond this a great new field of research awaits us in the study of the planktonic growth that girdles the salt acreage of the world in constant supply. Together with the food problems, we must also include the possible use of plankton as fuel. And finally the development of mining techniques that can release many more minerals than the magnesium and bromine which already have been made available.

These are the objectives before us, but nothing will be done unless we can rise to the occasion with an inner coordination of purpose great enough for this magnificent task. The day of the pioneer huntsman is over. The day of the bonanza frontier tycoon, of sheer will and energy raping plenty, is also behind us. We cannot as people breed the new energy and reap the awaiting sustenance from the sea without wedding science and engineering to a social and political thinking that goes beyond the race for individual riches or isolated national domination. The pattern has been established by the selfless world-wide work of the Food and Agricultural Organization, the F.A.O. of the United Nations. The time is ripe for scientific foundations in teamwork with university laboratories and governments to approach the frontier of ocean wealth as a civilized team, a committee of the whole.

# BIBLIOGRAPHY

# Bibliography

## CHAPTER I

BAKER, O. E. *The Population Prospect in Relation to the World's Agricultural Resources.*

BRITTAIN, R. *Let There Be Bread.* New York: Simon & Schuster, Inc., 1952.

COOK, R. C. *Human Fertility, the Modern Dilemma.* New York: William Sloane Associates, Inc., 1952.

HIATT, P. K. *World Population and Future Resources.* New York: American Book Company, 1952.

MERRIMAN, D. Food Shortages and the Sea. *Yale Review* (March 1950), pp. 430–444.

*Population Bulletin,* Washington, D. C. Various articles on population and resources.

ROSIN, J. and EASTMAN, M. *The Road to Abundance.* New York, McGraw-Hill Book Co., 1953.

OSBORN, FAIRFIELD. *The Limits of the Earth.* Boston: Little, Brown & Co., 1953.

———. *Our Plundered Planet.* Boston: Little, Brown & Co., 1948.

THOMPSON, W. S. Science and the Control of Human Population. American Association for the Advancement of Science, Centennial Collection, 1950.

UNITED NATIONS. Scientific Conference on the Conservation and Utilization of Resources Proceedings. Vol. 1, Plenary Proceedings U. N., 1951.

VOGT, WILLIAM. *Road to Survival.* New York: William Sloane Associates, Inc., 1948.

WOYTINSKY, W. S. and E. S. World Population and Production Trends and Outlook. Twentieth Century Fund, 1953.

### CHAPTER II

CLARKE, G. L. Conservation and Productivity of the Sea. *The Gamma Alpha Record*. Vol. 40, pp. 95–101, 1950.

COKER, R. E. *This Great and Wide Sea*. Chapel Hill: University of North Carolina Press, 1947.

COLMAN, J. S. *The Sea and Its Mysteries*. London: G. Bell & Sons, Ltd., 1950.

DAWES, BENJAMIN. *A Hundred Years of Biology,* Chapter XV, "Marine Biology." London: Duckworth & Co., Ltd., 1952.

DOUGLAS, T. S. *The Wealth of the Sea*. London: John Gifford, Ltd., 1946.

OMMANNEY, F. D. *The Ocean*. New York: Oxford University Press, 1949.

RILEY, G. A. *Survey of Biological Progress,* Vol. II, pp. 79–104. New York: Academic Press, Inc., 1952.

————. Food From the Sea. *Scientific American* (Oct. 1949), pp. 14–19.

RUSSELL, F. S. and YONGE, C. M. *The Seas*. London and New York: Frederick K. Warne & Co., 1944.

SVERDRUP, H. U. Some Aspects of the Primary Productivity of the Sea. F. A. O. *Fisheries Bulletin*. Vol. 5, No. 6, 1952.

WILSON, D. P. *Life of the Shore and Shallow Sea*. Chapters XI and XII. New York: The McBride Company, Inc., 1952.

### CHAPTER III

CHAPMAN, W. M. The Wealth of the Ocean. *Scientific Monthly* (March 1947).

CLARKE, G. L. Dynamics of Production in Marine Areas. *Ecological Monographs,* No. 16 (1946).

————. Conservation and the Production of the Sea. *The Gamma Alpha Record* (1940).

CUNNINGHAM, D. B. Deep Freeze Factory Ships. Paper No. 53

Fishing Boat Congress, Paris and Miami, Florida, F. A. O. (1953).

GALTSOFF, P. *Food Resources of the Ocean* (see P. K. Hiatt). New York: American Book Company, 1952.

GRAHAM, MICHAEL. *The Fish Gate.* London: Faber and Faber, Ltd., 1943.

GROSS, RAYMONT, MARSHAL and ORR. Fish Breeding in Sea Lochs. *Nature* (1944).

HARDY, A. C. The Hardy Plankton Indicator and Sampler. *Hull Bulletin of Marine Ecology,* Vol. IV (1953).

HARRISS, V. E. Some Practical Aspects of Electrical Fishing. *Atlantic Fisherman* (Feb. 1953).

HICKLING. Fish Farming. *Nature* (May 15, 1948).

SANDBERG, A. M. Fisheries of the World. Fishery Leaflet 109, U.S. Fish and Wildlife Service, Washington, D. C.

TRESSLER, D. K. and LEMON, J. McW. *Marine Products of Commerce.* New York: Reinhold Publishing Corp., 1951.

United Nations Scientific Conference on Conservation and Utilization of Resources, Proc. Vol. 7, Wild Life and Fish Resources, 1951.

United Nations Food and Agricultural Organization. Improving the Fisheries Contribution to World Food Supplies. *Fisheries Bulletin,* Vol. 6, No. 5 (1953).

World Fisheries Year Book. London: British-Continental Trade Press, Ltd., 1948–9.

WALFORD, L. A .The Deep-Sea Layer of Life. *Scientific American* (Aug. 1951).

YONGE, C. M. *Economics of the Sea Shore.* London: William Collins Sons & Co., Ltd., 1949.

Also see Bibliography Chapter II

## CHAPTER IV

Same as Chapter III
Also see Bibliography Chapter II

## CHAPTER V

Same as Chapter III

Also see Bibliography Chapter II

## CHAPTER VI

BURLEW, J. S. Algal Culture. Washington, D. C.: Carnegie Institute, Pub. 600 (1953).

CHAPMAN, V. J. *Seaweeds and Their Uses.* London: Methuen & Co., Ltd., 1950.

CLARKE, G. L. and BISHOP, D. W. The Nutritional Value of Plankton. *Ecology,* Vol. 29 (Jan. 1948).

HARDY, A. C. Plankton as a Source of Food. *Nature,* Vol. 147 (June 1941).

————. The Hardy Plankton Indicator and Sampler. *Hull Bulletin of Marine Ecology.* Vol. IV (1953).

HARVEY, H. W. Production of Living Matter in Sea. *Journal of the Marine Biological Association.* Vol. 29 (1950).

KETCHUM, BOSTWICK. Plankton Algae and Their Biological Significance. Chapter 18, Manual of Phycology. Chronica Botanica (1951).

MAXWELL, GAVIN. *Harpoon at a Venture.* London: Rupert Harte-Davis, Ltd., 1952.

MILNER, H. W. Algae as Food. *Scientific American* (Oct. 1953).

————. Chlorella As a Source of Proteins and Fats. *Vortex* XIII (Oct. 1952).

————. Possibilities in Photosynthetic Methods for Production of Oils and Proteins. *Journal of the American Oil and Chemical Society* (Aug. 1953).

PETTERSON, GROSS and KOCXY. Plankton Culture. *Nature.* Vol. 144 (1939).

SPOEHR, H. A. Chlorella As a Source of Food. Proceedings of the American Philos. Society, No. 95 (Feb. 1951).

Also see Bibliography Chapters II and III

### CHAPTER VII

American Association for the Advancement of Science, Centennial (1950).

AYRES, E. and SCARLOTT, C. A. *Energy Sources, the Wealth of the World*. New York: McGraw-Hill Book Co., 1952.

Fourth World Power Conference, Transactions. London: Percy Lund Humphries & Co., Ltd., 1952.

HIATT, P. K. *World Population and Future Resources*. New York: American Book Company, 1952.

United Nations Scientific Conference on Conservation and Utilization of Natural Resources Fuel and Energy Resources. Proceedings, Vol. III. New York: Columbia University Press, 1952.

Also see Bibliography Chapter VI

### CHAPTER VIII

AYRES, E. and SCARLOTT, C. A. *Energy Sources, the Wealth of the World*. New York: McGraw-Hill Book Co., 1952.

BEAU, C. and NIZANY, M. Industrial Utilization of the Differences in Temperatures Between the Deep and the Surface Waters of the Sea. Fourth World Power Conference, Transactions, Vol. 4.

Fourth World Power Conference, Transactions, Vol. 1. London: Percy Lund Humphries & Co., Ltd., 1952.

Also see Bibliography Chapter VII

### CHAPTER IX

ARMSTRONG, E. F. and MIALL, L. M. *Raw Materials From the Sea*. Leicester, England: Constructive Publications, Ltd., 1947.

HUTCHINSON, G. E. The Cycle of Materials. American Association for the Advancement of Science, Centennial (1950).

LOVERING, T. S. The Cycle of Materials, American Association for the Advancement of Science, Centennial (1950).

MOORE, H. F. The Seas as a Conservator of Waste and a Reservoir of Food. Washington, D. C.: *Smithsonian Annual Report* (1917).

TRESSLER, D. K. and LEMON, J. McW. *Marine Products of Commerce*. New York: Reinhold Publishing Corp., 1951.

RAKESTRAW, N. W Mineral Resources of the Ocean. From *World Population and Future Resources*. New York: American Book Company, 1952.

United Nations Scientific Conference of Conservation and Utilization of Resources, Proceedings Vol. 2, Mineral Resources; Vol. 4, Water Resources. New York: Columbia University Press, 1950.

**CHAPTER X**

Same as Chapter I